WIDER WORLD

SECOND EDITION

S

STARTER

CONTENTS

Get started!

0

VOCABULARY
The alphabet | Spelling words/names | Numbers | Colours | Classroom objects | Classroom language

GRAMMAR
I'm ... | *I like ... / He/She likes ...* | *This is ...* |

0.1 How do you spell that?

1 Label the photos with the names below.

~~Alex~~ Jen Lian Lucas

1 *Alex* 2 ______

3 ______ 4 ______

2 Label the photos with the words below.

~~computer game~~ laptop computer Maths music

1 *computer game* 2 ______

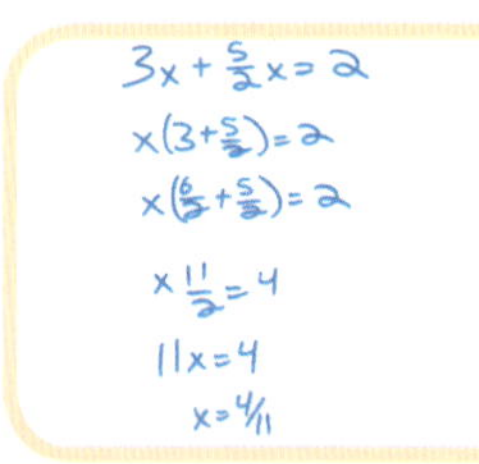

3 ______ 4 ______

3 Look and complete the sentences.

Hi. I'm Alex. I [1]*like* computers and computer [2]g*a*m*e*s!

Hello. [3]_ '_ Jen. I like [4]c_ _ _ _ _ _s!

[5]_ _. I'm Lian. I [6]l _ _ _ sports!

[7]_ _ _ _ _. I'm Lucas. I like [8]m _ _ _ _ and Maths!

4 Complete the alphabet.

A **B** [1]*C* D [2]__ F G
[3]__ I J **K** [4]__ M [5]__
O P [6]__ R [7]__ T
U [8]__ **W** X [9]__ Z

5 Complete the words with the letters below.

b f g ~~l~~ s t

1 *l* ion
2 _ ish
3 _ andwich
4 _ able
5 _ irl
6 _ oy

6 Match the sentence halves.

1 What's your *b*
2 My name's ☐
3 How do you ☐
4 I'm twelve ☐
5 I'm from ☐

a Bernadette.
b name?
c Spain.
d spell your name?
e years old.

0.2 Numbers and colours

1 Order the words to make sentences.

1 Superdug / also / Dug / is / .
Dug is also Superdug.
2 is / superhero / He / a / .
____
3 Kit / Dug's / friend / is / .
____
4 clever / She / is / very / .
____

2 Write the numbers.

five	twelve	one
5		
ten	**eight**	**four**
eleven	**six**	**three**
seven	**nine**	**six**

3 Complete the missing numbers.

1 two four *six* eight ten ______
2 one three ______ seven ______ eleven

4 Write the numbers in words.

1 eleven	*11*	6 seventeen	______
2 fourteen	______	7 twenty	______
3 nineteen	______	8 thirteen	______
4 fifteen	______	9 sixteen	______
5 twelve	______	10 eighteen	______

5 Match colours 1–6 with the words.

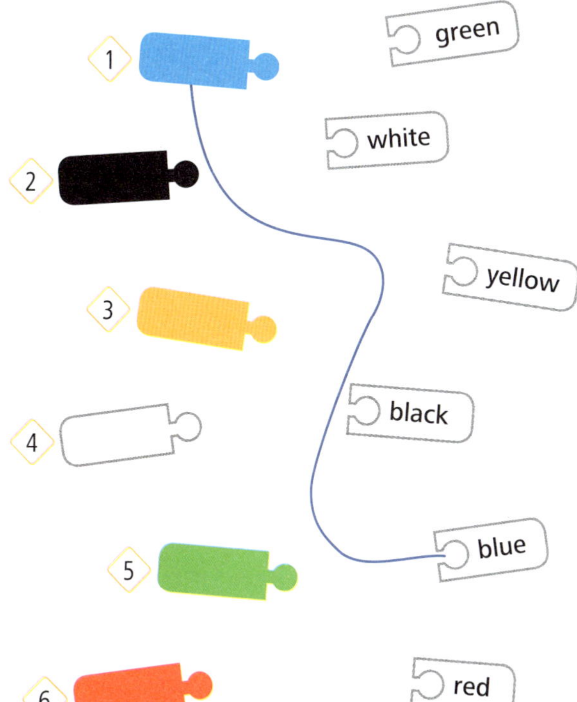

6 Look at the words below and write their colours.

five eleven ~~four~~ sixteen twelve twenty
nineteen eight thirteen seventeen

1 4 *red*
2 12 ______
3 16 ______
4 11 ______
5 13 ______
6 5 ______
7 17 ______
8 19 ______
9 20 ______
10 8 ______

In the classroom

1 Choose the correct option.

1 sandwich / book

2 pencil / pen

3 notebook / ruler

4 bag / sandwich

5 pen / pencil

6 notebook / ruler

2 Write the plurals.

1 a pencil — three *pencils*
2 a book — nine ________
3 a sandwich — ten ________
4 a pencil — ten ________
5 a notebook — five ________
6 a pen — seven ________
7 a box — thirteen ________
8 a ruler — eleven ________
9 a table — two ________
10 a cupcake — six ________

3 Complete the sentences with *It's* or *They're*.

1 *It's* a bin.
2 ________ clocks.
3 ________ a board.
4 ________ a desk.
5 ________ chairs.
6 ________ bins.

4 Find five words in the word snake. Then label the classroom objects.

1 *desk*

2 ________

3 ________

4 ________

5 ________

5 Read the expressions. Who usually says them? Mark the expressions T (teacher) or S (student).

1 Open your books. T / S
2 Can you help me, please? T / S
3 Stand up. T / S
4 Work in pairs. T / S
5 What's … in English? T / S
6 Write your name. T / S

6 Order the sentences to make a dialogue.

a ☐ Can you repeat that, please?
b ☐ What does 'brilliant' mean?
c ☐ It means 'very good'.
d [1] Hello, Mrs Gold. Can you help me, please?
e ☐ Yes, Tom. How can I help?
f ☐ Yes. It means 'very good'.

 I can talk about classroom objects and understand classroom instructions.

Self-check

Vocabulary

1 Choose the correct option.

0 thirteen (13) / 11
1 twelve 20 / 12
2 seventeen 17 / 15
3 blue / green
4 red / yellow
5 black / white

2 Look at the photos and write the words.

0 *pen*

1 ________

2 ________

3 ________

4 ________

5 ________

Grammar

3 Choose the correct option.

0 (*It's a*) / *They're* cupcake.
1 *It's a* / *They're* tables.
2 *It's a* / *They're* zebra.
3 *It's a* / *They're* desks.
4 *It's a* / *They're* elephants.
5 *It's a* / *They're* flower.

4 Look at the photos and write the plurals.

0 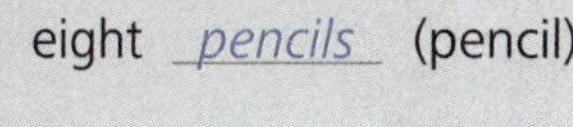 eight *pencils* (pencil)

1  six ________ (book)

2  two ________ (box)

3  three ________ (bin)

4  two ________ (sandwich)

5  four ________ (tree)

Speaking

5 Complete the sentences with the words below.

books down ~~help~~ pairs please up

Can you [0]*help* me, [1]________?

Sit [2]________.

Close your [3]________.

Work in [4]________.

Stand [5]________.

YOUR SCORE

Vocabulary:	__/10	Speaking:	__/5
Grammar:	__/10	**Total:**	**__/25**

Family and friends

1

VOCABULARY
Family | Countries and nationalities | Places | Art

GRAMMAR
to be affirmative | *to be* negative | *my, your* | possessive *'s*

1.1 Vocabulary

Family

1 Who is who in Sally's family? Match 1–7 with A–G.

1 Sally's father [B]
2 Sally's mother [ ]
3 Sally's parents [ ] [ ]
4 Sally's grandfather [ ]
5 Sally's grandmother [ ]
6 Sally's brothers [ ] [ ]
7 Sally's sister [ ]

2 Match the letters to make family words.

1 daught	nt
2 cous	ad
3 unc	on
4 grand	in
5 au	er
6 gran	ny
7 s	le

3 Look at Will's family tree. Complete the sentences with one word in each gap.

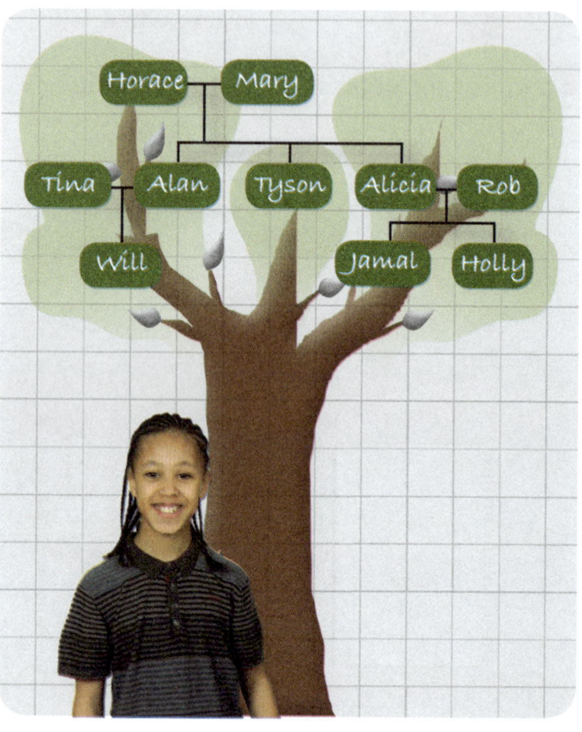

1 Alan: Horace is my [1] *father*. He's Will's [2]________ .

2 Holly: Tina is my [3]________ . Jamal and I are Will's [4]________ . I am Alicia and Rob's [5]________ .

3 Jamal: Holly is my [6]________ . I'm Alicia's [7]________ .

4 Complete the sentences with one word in each gap.

1 Amy is Emily's mother. Emily is Amy's *daughter*.
2 Tom is Danny's father. Danny is Tom's ________ .
3 Lakshmi is Amar's mother and Viraj's aunt. Amar and Viraj are ________ .
4 Ada is Sam's mother. Sam is Rosa's father. Ada is Rosa's ________ .
5 Jakub is Filip's brother. Filip is Alina's father. Jakub is Alina's ________ .

 I can talk about the people in a family.

On the Portal
Extra Practice Activities: Lesson 1.1

1.2 Grammar

to be affirmative

1 Look at the pictures. Choose the correct option.

A birthday party

1 Look. We *am* / (*are*) / *is* at Tom's house.

2 Tom *am* / *are* / *is* twelve today.

3 I *am* / *are* / *is* happy!
12

A new student

4 He *am* / *are* / *is* a teacher.

5 She *am* / *are* / *is* a student.

6 They *am* / *are* / *is* in the classroom.

2 Look at Exercise 1. Complete the sentences with the short form of the verb *to be*.

1 Look. We*'re* at Tom's house.

2 Tom______ twelve today.

3 I______ happy!

4 He______ a teacher.

5 She______ a student.

6 They______ in the classroom.

7 You______ in this classroom.

I can use the affirmative form of the verb *to be* and *my*, *your*.

3 Complete the dialogue with *am*, *are* or *is*.

Harry: Hi. I [1]*am* Harry.

Jack: Hi, Harry. I [2]______ Jack. You [3]______ in Class 2 with me. Welcome!

Harry: Thanks.

Jack: This is Tony. He [4]______ my classmate. We [5]______ best friends too. Mrs Lee and Mr Brown [6]______ my favourite teachers.

4 Complete the sentences with *my* or *your*.

This is [1]______ granny, Sophie.
This is [2]______ present, Granny.

5 Complete the sentences with the words below.

~~am~~ are is my they

Hi! I [1]*am* Tom. This is [2]______ family. My parents' names [3]______ Amy and Andrew. [4]______ are teachers. My sister [5]______ thirteen.

On the Portal
Extra Practice Activities: Lesson 1.2

Grammar

to be negative

1 Rewrite the sentences. Use the short form of the verb *to be*.

1 My friends are not in the classroom.
My friends aren't in the classroom.
2 You are not right.
______
3 I am not a superhero.
______
4 Ben is not my friend.
______
5 She is not my aunt.
______
6 They are not my cousins.
______

2 Write negative sentences. Use the short form of the verb *to be*.

1 She's eleven. She's in the classroom.
She *isn't eleven*.
She ______.

2 They're happy. They're in the house.
They ______.
They ______.

3 He's a teacher. He's ready for school.
He ______.
He ______.

Vocabulary

3 Complete the words and write the nationalities.

1 P *o l a n d* — *Polish*
2 F _ _ _ _ e — ______
3 the _ _ — ______
4 T _ _ _ _ y — ______
5 C _ _ _ a — ______
6 the _ _ _ — ______
7 S _ _ _ n — ______

4 Write sentences that are true for you. Use *am, 'm not, are, aren't, is* or *isn't*.

1 My school *is / isn't* in the USA.
2 My English teacher ______ British.
3 My friends ______ in China.
4 My parents ______ Polish.
5 I ______ Turkish.
6 I ______ twelve.

5 Complete the dialogue with the affirmative (✓) or negative (✗) form of the verb *to be*.

Kit: Look! It [1]*is* (✓) you, Dug! You [2]______ (✓) with your grandad and granny, right?
Dug: No, I [3]______ (✗). They [4]______ (✓) my parents. My dad [5]______ (✓) British, but my mother [6]______ (✗) British. She [7]______ (✓) Polish.
Kit: It [8]______ (✗) a new photo.
Dug: That's right. The photo [9]______ (✓) very old.

I can talk about countries and nationalities and use the negative form of the verb *to be*.

On the Portal
Extra Practice Activities: Lesson 1.3

Speaking

Introductions

1 1.2 Listen and repeat the phrases.

SPEAKING Introductions

A: *Mum*, this is *Lucas*.
He is my *friend/classmate*.
Lucas, this is *my mum*.
B: Hello, *Lucas*. Nice to meet you.
C: Nice to meet you too.

2 Complete the dialogues. Choose the correct answer.

1 a Sorry, Mum!
b Hi, Mum!
c It's OK, Mum!
2 a This is Amy.
b I'm Amy.
c You're here, Amy.

3 a You're Amy.
b Hello, Amy.
c Thank you, Amy.
4 a Nice to meet you, Jill.
b Nice to meet you, Mrs Wilson.
c Nice to meet you, Amy.

I can make introductions.

3 Complete the dialogue with the words below.

he's hi nice ~~this is~~ to meet you

Thomas: Hi, Stella, [1]*this is* Frankie. [2]______ my cousin.
Stella: [3]______, Frankie. Nice [4]______.
Frankie: [5]______ to meet you too, Stella.

4 Complete the dialogue with sentences a–d.

May: [1]*b*
Aunt Sue: Oh, hello, May!
May: This is Nancy. [2]___
Aunt Sue: Hello, Nancy. [3]___
Nancy: Hello, Mrs Smith. [4]___

a She's my best friend at school.
b Hi, Aunt Sue.
c Nice to meet you.
d Nice to meet you too.

5 Write a dialogue like in Exercise 4. Introduce your English friend to your teacher.

You: ______
Teacher: ______
You: ______
______
Teacher: ______
______
Your friend: ______
______

On the Portal
Extra Practice Activities: Lesson 1.4

1.5 Reading and Vocabulary

Family photo album

My photo album

1 ☐
In this photo, my mum and dad are with Aunt Ellie. They aren't at home, they're on holiday in Spain. They are happy. Aunt Ellie is my dad's sister. My dad's family is Spanish.

2 ☐
This is my friend Bea. She's at home. Her mum is Turkish and her dad is British. She's fun. Buttons is in the photo too. He's Bea's cat.

3 ☐
Hi. I'm Sahar and this is my brother, Yusuf. I'm fourteen and he's ten. We're from Manchester. It's in the UK.

1 Read the texts. Match texts 1–3 with photos A–C.

2 Read the texts again. Match 1–6 with a–f.

1 Hi. My name's [c]
2 I'm ☐
3 My brother is ☐
4 Ellie is ☐
5 Bea is ☐
6 Buttons is ☐

a my aunt.
b my friend.
c Sahar.
d fourteen.
e a cat.
f ten.

3 Complete the sentences with *British*, *Turkish* or *Spanish*. Check your answers in the texts.

1 Sahar is *British*.
2 Yusuf is ________.
3 Sahar's dad is ________.
4 Aunt Ellie is ________.
5 Bea's mother is ________.
6 Bea's father is ________.

Vocabulary

4 Look at the photos and complete the words for places.

1 I'm at h _ _ _ today.

2 We aren't at s _ _ _ _ _ today.

3 My cousins are on h _ _ _ _ _ _.

4 My granny and my grandad are in the p _ _ _.

 I can understand a text about family photos and places.

On the Portal
Extra Practice Activities: Lesson 1.5

1.6 Listening and Writing

Best friends

1 1.3 Listen to Rob. Mark the sentences T (true) or F (false).

1

1 Rob and Victor are best friends. T / F
2 They're at Rob's house. T / F
3 Rob's mum and Victor's mum are best friends. T / F

2

4 Rob's on holiday. T / F
5 Rob and Mel are in the UK. T / F
6 Rob and Mel are cousins. T / F

2 1.3 Listen again. Complete the tables.

	Rob
Age	*12*
Nationality	

	Victor
Age	
Nationality	

	Mel
Age	
Nationality	

I can understand and write short texts about best friends.

3 Correct the text. Add capital letters.

Clara
~~clara~~ and ada are best friends. clara is twelve and ada is thirteen. clara is from the uk. she's british. ada is from turkey. she's turkish.

4 Read the text in Exercise 3 again. Complete the table.

	Clara	Ada
Age	*12*	
Country		
Nationality		

WRITING TIME

5 Write about best friends Pierre and Pedro.

	Pierre	Pedro
Age	12	11
Country	France	Spain
Nationality	French	Spanish

1 **Find ideas**
Look at the table with information about Pierre and Pedro.

2 **Draft**
Write about their age, country and nationality.
Pierre and Pedro are best friends.
Pierre/Pedro is …
He's from …

3 **Check and write**
Check all the capital letters and write the final version of your text.

On the Portal
Extra Practice Activities: Lesson 1.6

CLIL: Art

Families in Art

1 Look at the painting and the people. Match people 1–6 with words A–F in the painting.

2 Look at Exercise 1 and do the crossword.

Across

3 Alberto and Maria are Stefano's ________.

6 Rosanna is Anna and Stefano's ________.

7 Luca is Rosanna's ________.

Down

1 Stefano is Maria's *son*.

2 Maria is Stefano's ________.

4 Rosanna is Luca's ________.

5 Stefano is Luca's ________.

3 What nationality are the artists? Complete the sentences.

1 Leonardo da Vinci is an I t *a* l *i* *a* n artist.

2 Müfide Kadri is a T _ _ _ _ s h artist.

3 David Hockney is a B _ i t _ _ _ artist.

4 Shen Zhou is a C _ i n _ _ e artist.

5 Pablo Picasso is a S _ a n _ _ _ artist.

6 Georgia O'Keeffe is an A m _ _ _ _ a n artist.

 I can talk about families in art.

My Language File

WORDLIST 1.4

Family

aunt (n)
brother (n)
cousin (n)
dad (n)
daughter (n)
father (n)
grandad (n)
grandfather (n)
grandmother (n)
granny (n)
mother (n)
mum (n)
parents (n)
sister (n)
son (n)
uncle (n)

Countries and nationalities

American (adj)
British (adj)
China (n)
Chinese (adj)
France (n)
French (adj)
Poland (n)
Polish (adj)
Spain (n)
Spanish (adj)
Turkey (n)
Turkish (adj)
the UK (n)
the USA (n)

Places

at home
at school
in the park
on holiday

Art

artist (n)
by (prep)
children (singular: child) (n)
painting (n)
people (singular: person) (n)
picture (n)

Extra words

best friend
birthday (n)
box (n)
cake (n)
card (n)
classmate (n)
fat (adj)
flag (n)
hamster (n)
happy (adj)
holiday (n)
home (n)
Let's have a break.
mouse (n)
neighbour (n)
Nice to meet you.
orange (adj)
portrait (n)
present (n)

Sounds good!

Be careful!
Hold this, please.
I've got it!

MY LANGUAGE NOTES

Self-check

Vocabulary

1 Complete the pairs.

0 mum and *dad*
1 ________ and uncle
2 mother and ________
3 ________ and sister
4 son and ________
5 ________ and grandad

2 Look at the photos and complete the words.

0 She's from P *o l a n d*.

1 He's in the p _ _ _ _.

2 She's A _ _ _ _ _ _ _ _.

3 They're at s _ _ _ _ _ _.

4 Paris is in F _ _ _ _ _ _.

5 She's at h _ _ _.

Grammar

3 Complete the sentences with the affirmative (✓) or negative (✗) form of the verb *to be*.

0 This *isn't* (✗) my garden. It's a park!
1 My best friends ________ (✓) Yasemin and Jane.
2 Yasemin ________ (✓) Turkish.
3 Jane and I ________ (✗) Turkish.
4 We ________ (✓) from the UK.
5 I ________ (✗) in the UK in this photo!

4 Choose the correct option.

Jack: [0]*(I)* / *You* am Jack and this is [1]*my / your* cousin, Ben. [2]*They / We* are with Freddie. Freddie is [3]*Ben / Ben's* dog.

Jack: Clara, you are with [4]*my / your* friend, Nadia in this picture, right?
Clara: Yes. Mum and [5]*Nadia / Nadia's* mum are in the picture too.

Speaking

5 Complete the dialogue with one word in each gap.

Diane: Jack, [0]*this* [1]________ my friend, Harry.
Jack: [2]________, Harry. [3]________ to meet you.
Harry: Hi, Jack. Nice to [4]________ you [5]________.

YOUR SCORE

Vocabulary: __/10	Speaking: __/5
Grammar: __/10	**Total: __/25**

On the Portal
Extra Practice Activities: Self-check

BBC CULTURE

English around the world

1 Look at the flags and write the countries.

1 the U _ _

2 C _ n _ d _

3 Ir _ l _ nd

4 Ne _ Zea _ a _ _

5 Sou _ _ A _ _ i _ a

6 A _ s _ r _ l _ a

2 Choose the correct answer.

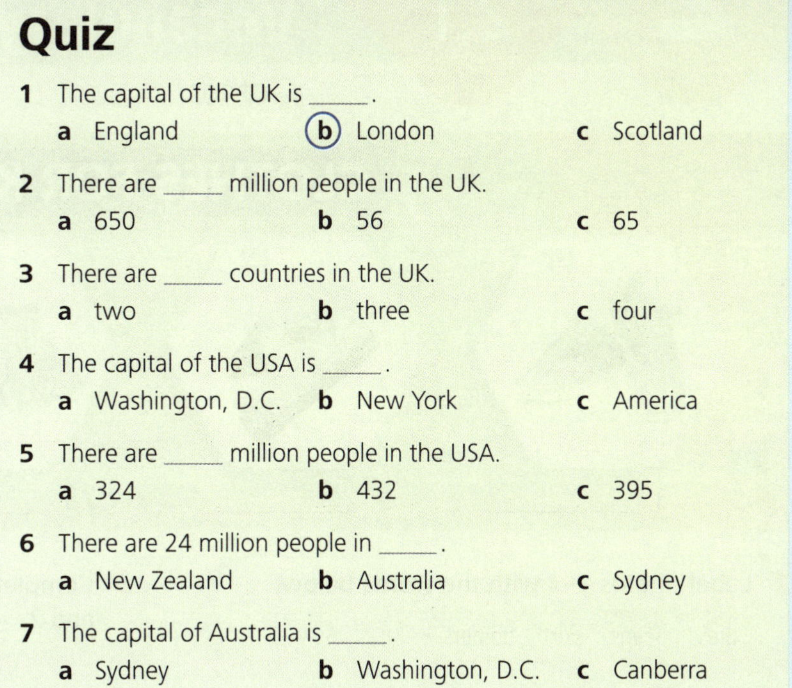

Quiz

1 The capital of the UK is _____.
a England **(b)** London **c** Scotland

2 There are _____ million people in the UK.
a 650 **b** 56 **c** 65

3 There are _____ countries in the UK.
a two **b** three **c** four

4 The capital of the USA is _____.
a Washington, D.C. **b** New York **c** America

5 There are _____ million people in the USA.
a 324 **b** 432 **c** 395

6 There are 24 million people in _____.
a New Zealand **b** Australia **c** Sydney

7 The capital of Australia is _____.
a Sydney **b** Washington, D.C. **c** Canberra

3 Look at the map of the United Kingdom. Complete the names of the countries.

1 S _ _ t _ _ n _

2 N _ _ t _ _ _ n I _ _ _ a _ d

3 W _ l _ _

4 E _ g _ _ _ d

My things

2

VOCABULARY
Clothes | Adjectives | My things | Shapes

GRAMMAR
this, that, these, those | *too big/ small* | *to be* questions and short answers

2.1 Vocabulary

Clothes

1 ________ 2 ________ 3 ________ 4 ________

1 Label photos 1–4 with the words below.

dress jeans skirt trainers

2 Find nine clothes words in the word search. Look → and ↓. Then complete the words.

T	T	R	A	C	K	S	U	I	T
E	H	B	W	Q	L	W	T	F	D
L	T	V	I	H	S	H	O	E	S
R	R	B	U	E	S	Y	P	U	S
Y	O	I	Y	R	C	L	T	B	K
D	U	T	F	F	A	E	U	X	I
R	S	M	V	C	P	C	G	Q	R
E	E	I	J	A	C	K	E	T	T
S	R	M	Q	W	S	N	Q	D	P
S	S	C	O	A	T	F	I	S	Y

1 t*racksui*t
2 s _ _ _ s
3 j _ _ _ _ t
4 c _ _ t
5 d _ _ _ s
6 t _ _ _ _ _ _ _ s
7 c _ p
8 t _ p
9 s _ _ _ t

3 Complete the sentences. Use words from Exercises 1 and 2.

1 Anne's *dress* is yellow.
2 Anne's ________ is green.
3 Anne's ________ are black.
4 Eddie's ________ is blue.
5 Eddie's ________ is red.
6 Eddie's ________ are black.
7 Eddie's ________ are white.

4 What are they? Label photos 1–4.

1 ________

2 ________

3 ________

4 ________

 I can talk about clothes.

On the Portal
Extra Practice Activities: Lesson 2.1

Grammar

this, that, these, those

1 Complete the sentences with *this, that, these* or *those*.

1 *That* is Alex's bag.

2 ________ is my dad's bag.

3 ________ shoes are my mum's.

4 ________ shoes are Jen's.

5 ________ dress is Jen's.

6 ________ is my mum's dress.

Vocabulary

2 Label the pictures with the words below.

big ~~boring~~ cool long new old short small

1 *boring* and ________ 2 ________ and ________

3 ________ and ________ 4 ________ and ________

3 Complete the sentences with *is* or *are*, *too* and adjectives from Exercise 2.

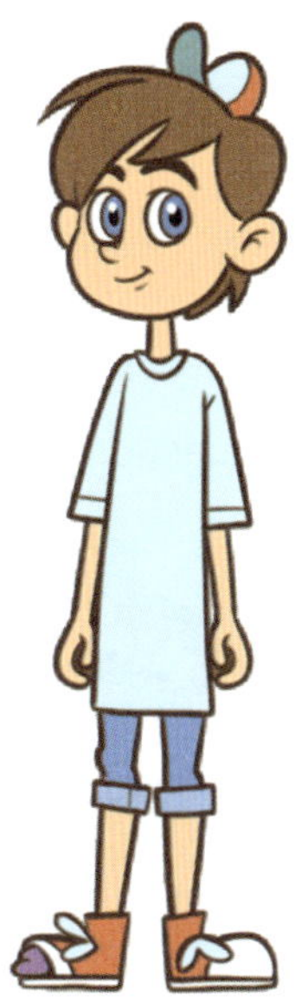

1 John's cap is *too small*.
2 John's jeans ________.
3 John's T-shirt ________.
4 John's trainers ________.

4 Look at the photos and write sentences. Use *this, that, these* or *those* and the phrases below.

~~a boring cap~~ an old trainer new trousers small shoes

1 *This is a boring cap.*
2 ________
3 ________
4 ________

I can use *this, that, these, those* and adjectives.

On the Portal
Extra Practice Activities: Lesson 2.2

2.3 Grammar

to be questions and short answers

1 Add a question mark (?) or a full stop (.).

1 Is he French?
2 My brother is eight years old
3 Are you a student
4 Is Lee your friend
5 I'm not Italian
6 Are they happy

2 Complete the questions with *is* or *are*.

1 Is Kit a cat?
2 ______ she black?
3 ______ Kit and Dug friends?
4 ______ they at school?
5 ______ Dug's suit blue and red?
6 ______ his suit too small?

3 Match answers a–f with questions 1–6 in Exercise 2.

a ☐ Yes, it is.
b ☐ Yes, they are.
c [1] Yes, she is.
d ☐ No, it isn't.
e ☐ No, they aren't.
f ☐ No, she isn't.

4 Think about Dug and Kit. Complete the answers with your own ideas.

1 Are Dug and Kit cool?
______, they ______.
2 Is Dug clever?
______, he ______.
3 Is Kit a good friend?
______, she ______.
4 Is Dug's suit OK?
______, it ______.
5 Are you a superhero?
______, I ______.

5 Complete the dialogue. Use *am, are, is* or *isn't* and the words in brackets.

A: [1]Are you (you) May?
B: Yes, [2]______.
A: [3]______ (Ben) your brother?
B: No, [4]______. He's my classmate.
A: [5]______ (you) best friends?
B: Yes, [6]______.
A: [7]______ (he) Spanish?
B: Yes, [8]______. He's from Madrid.

6 Order the words to make questions.

1 is / What / name / your / ?
What is your name?
2 at / Are / school / you / ?
______
3 twelve / you / Are / ?
______
4 your / best / thirteen / friend / Is / ?
______
5 best / name / What / friend's / is / your / ?
______

7 Answer the questions in Exercise 6 for you.

1 My name ______
2 ______
3 ______
4 ______
5 ______

 I can ask and answer questions with the verb *to be*.

On the Portal
Extra Practice Activities: Lesson 2.3

2.4 Speaking

Asking for personal information

1 2.1 Listen and repeat the phrases.

SPEAKING Asking for personal information

What's your name?
How old are you?
Where are you from?
What's your favourite *music/sport/film*?
Who's your favourite *actor/singer/sportsperson*?

2 Complete the dialogue with sentences a–e.

Man: Hi. Welcome to the show. [1]*e*
Nancy: My name's Nancy.
Man: Where are you from?
Nancy: [2]___
Man: [3]___
Nancy: I'm twelve.
Man: What's your favourite sport?
Nancy: [4]___
Man: Who's your favourite actor?
Nancy: [5]___

a Swimming.
b London, England.
c Asa Butterfield.
d How old are you?
e What's your name?

I can ask for and give personal information.

3 Choose the correct option.

1 *What* / *Who* is your name?
2 *What* / *Where* are you from?
3 *How* / *Where* old are you?
4 *Who* / *Where* is your favourite sports person?
5 *What* / *Who* is your favourite film?

4 Match answers a–e with questions 1–5 in Exercise 3.

a [ ] Manchester, England.
b [1] I'm Danny.
c [ ] Renato Sanches. He's from Portugal.
d [ ] *Dolittle*.
e [ ] Twelve.

5 Read. Then complete the questions for Emma.

My Blog by Emma Carter
HOME
BLOG
GALLERY
MORE
Hi! I'm Emma and I'm new to Northwood School. I'm [1]twelve, and I'm [2]from Cardiff, Wales. My favourite sport is [3]tennis, and my favourite book is [4]*The Hobbit*. My favourite singer is [5]Alicia Keys.

1 How old *are you*?
2 Where __________?
3 What __________?
4 What __________?
5 Who __________?

6 Answer the questions in Exercise 5 for you.

1 I'm __________
2 __________
3 __________
4 __________
5 __________

On the Portal
Extra Practice Activities: Lesson 2.4

2.5 Reading and Vocabulary

Clever clothes

OUR CLEVER CLOTHES

1 ☐

Hi, I'm Sam. Look at this – it's a cool jacket, but that's not all. It's an MP3 player too, with my favourite music. My jacket is green and my sister Anna's is red.

A

2 ☐

Hello. I'm Luke. These jeans are my favourite clothes. They're cool and they're clever too. Look. This is a pocket for my mobile phone. It's a phone charger too. My jeans are fantastic!

B

3 ☐

My name's Becky. These trainers are my favourite things. They're red and yellow and they're very cool. Look – what are these? They're small wheels! My trainers are skates too! My trainers are very clever!

C

1 Read the texts. Match children 1–3 with their clothes A–C.

2 Read the texts in Exercise 1 again. Then complete 1–3 with the names below. There is one extra name.

Anna Becky Luke Sam

1 My favourite things are red and yellow. I'm ________ .

2 I'm Sam's sister. I'm ________ .

3 My favourite clothes are my jeans. I'm ________ .

Vocabulary

3 Look at the photos. What can you see? Choose Y (yes) or N (no).

1 mountain bike Y / N
2 skateboard Y / N
3 laptop computer Y / N
4 games console Y / N

 I can understand a short text about clever clothes.

On the Portal
Extra Practice Activities: Lesson 2.5

Listening and Writing

My favourite things

1 Label the pictures with the words below.

backpack games console laptop computer
mobile phone mountain bike ~~trainers~~

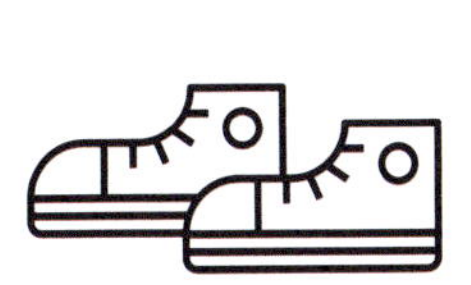

1 ☐ *trainers*

2 ☐ ______

3 ☐ ______

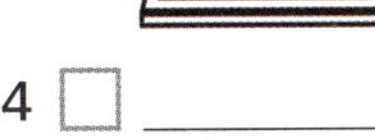

4 ☐ ______

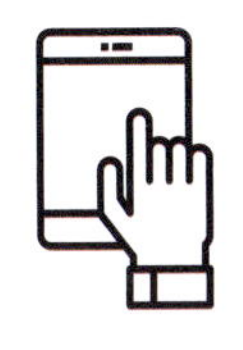

5 ☐ ______

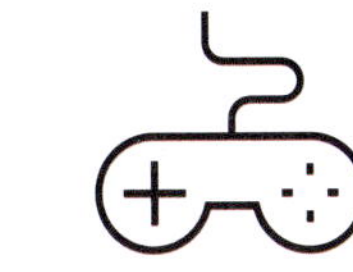

6 ☐ ______

2 2.2 Listen to Luke and Rosa. What do they talk about? Tick (✓) the pictures in Exercise 1.

3 2.2 Listen again. Choose the correct answer.

1 Luke's ______ is new.

A 

B 

2 Rosa's favourite colour is ______.

A 

B 

3 Luke's trainers are ______.

A 

B 

4 Rosa's favourite thing is this ______.

A 

B 

I can understand and write short texts about favourite things.

4 Correct Harry's blog post. Add punctuation marks.

, . ? !

Hi [1] *!*
My name is Harry [2] ☐ My favourite things are my new school bag [3] ☐ my mobile phone and my skateboard [4] ☐ What's my favourite colour [5] ☐ That's easy [6] ☐ It's red [7] ☐

WRITING TIME

5 Write a blog post about your favourite things. Use punctuation marks.

1 Find ideas
Make a list of your favourite things and colours. Think of adjectives to describe them.

2 Draft
Give your text a title.
Hello/Hi!
My name is …
My favourite things are …
My favourite colour is …

3 Check and write
Check your punctuation and write the final version of your text.

On the Portal
Extra Practice Activities: Lesson 2.6

CLIL: Geometry

Shapes

1 Look at the shapes and do the puzzle.

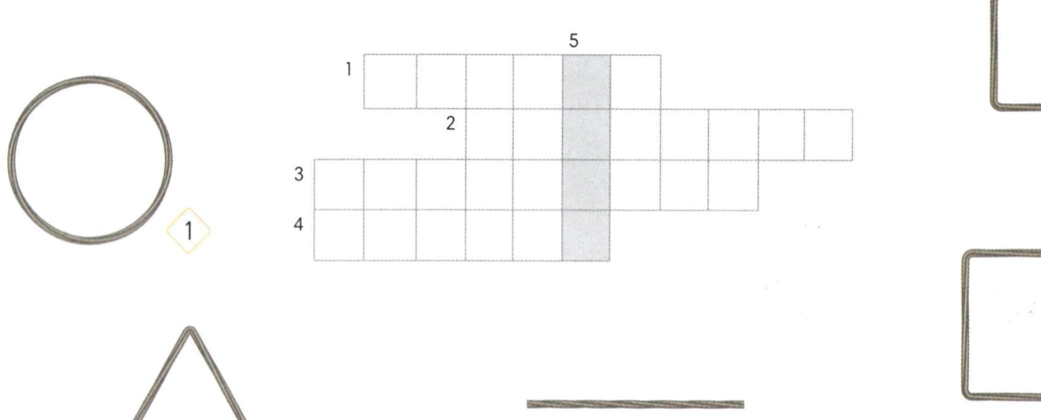

2 Match people 1–5 with things A–E.

1 *B*

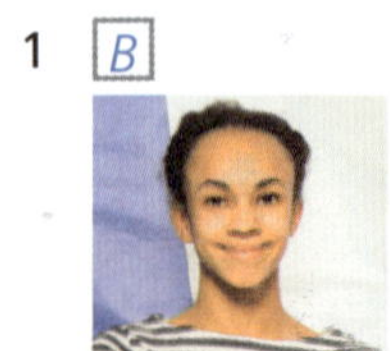

This is my skirt. It's white with small squares and circles.

A 

2 ☐

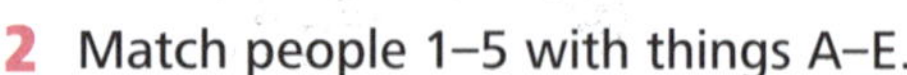

These are my new trainers. They're blue with red lines.

B 

3 ☐

This is my new jacket. It's black with small triangles.

C 

4 ☐

This is my school bag. It's blue with big rectangles and small circles.

D 

5 ☐

This is my T-shirt. It's black with white lines and red circles.

E 

3 Look at things A–E in Exercise 2 again and answer the questions.

1 Look at the jacket.
What colour are the triangles? *white*

2 Look at the skirt.
What colour are the squares? ______
What colour are the circles? ______

3 Look at the T-shirt.
What colour are the lines? ______
What colour are the circles? ______

4 Look at the trainers.
What colour are the lines? ______

5 Look at the school bag.
What colour are the rectangles? ______
What colour are the circles? ______

4 Look at pictures A and B and count the shapes!

A

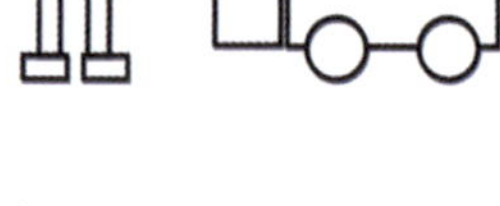

B

Picture A		**Picture B**	
1 circles	*3*	6 circles	______
2 squares	______	7 squares	______
3 rectangles	______	8 rectangles	______
4 lines	______	9 lines	______
5 triangles	______	10 triangles	______

 I can describe different shapes.

My Language File

WORDLIST 2.3

Clothes

cap (n) ______
coat (n) ______
dress (n) ______
jacket (n) ______
jeans (n) ______
shoes (n) ______
skirt (n) ______
T-shirt (n) ______
top (n) ______
tracksuit (n) ______
tracksuit jacket (n) ______
tracksuit trousers (n) ______
trainers (n) ______
trousers (n) ______

Adjectives

big (adj) ______
boring (adj) ______
cool (adj) ______
long (adj) ______
new (adj) ______
old (adj) ______
short (adj) ______
small (adj) ______

My things

backpack (n) ______
laptop computer (n) ______
mobile phone (n) ______
mountain bike (n) ______

Shapes

circle (n) ______
line (n) ______
rectangle (n) ______
square (n) ______
triangle (n) ______

Extra words

Are you sure? ______
at the weekend ______
box (n) ______
boy (n) ______
clever cat ______
cold (adj) ______
fantastic (adj) ______
favourite (adj) ______
gadget (n) ______
girl (n) ______
Good question. ______
High five! ______
How cool is that! ______
just right ______
No problem. ______
put away (v) ______
rock (music) (n) ______
school band (n) ______
size (n) ______
skateboard (n) ______
suit (n) ______
That's easy. ______
That's not all. ______
too (small) (adv) ______

Sounds good!

Hang on. ______
Here you are. ______
Over there. ______
What's up? ______

MY LANGUAGE NOTES

Self-check

Vocabulary

1 Choose the odd one out.

0 (T-shirt) trainers shoes
1 cool fantastic boring
2 backpack top dress
3 trousers jeans cap
4 long top big
5 jacket skirt new

2 Look at the photo and write the words.

0 *T-shirt*
1 ______
2 ______
3 ______
4 ______
5 ______

Grammar

3 Choose the correct answer.

0 My shoes ____ too small.
a is (b) are

1 ____ T-shirt isn't big.
a This b These

2 What ____ it?
a are b is

3 ____ are my brothers.
a That b Those

4 Jen's trainers ____ cool.
a are b is

5 ____ they your books?
a Is b Are

4 Answer yes (✓) or no (✗). Use short answers.

0 A: Are you OK?
B: *Yes, I am.* ✓

1 A: Is it your backpack?
B: ______ ✓

2 A: Are your new shoes black?
B: ______ ✗

3 A: Are we friends?
B: ______ ✓

4 A: Is Tom your brother?
B: ______ ✗

5 A: Is Ella at school?
B: ______ ✓

Speaking

5 Order the sentences to make a dialogue.

a ☐ Twelve. Are you twelve too?
b ☐ *The Lord of the Rings*.
c [*0*] Hello, I'm Benjamin. What's your name?
d ☐ Hi, I'm Jackie. I'm from the UK. Where are you from?
e ☐ I'm from the UK too. How old are you?
f ☐ No, I'm not. I'm thirteen. What's your favourite book?

YOUR SCORE

Vocabulary:	___/10	Speaking	___/5
Grammar:	___/10	**Total:**	**___/25**

On the Portal
Extra Practice Activities: Self-check

Quick Progress Check Units 1–2

Reading and Writing

In this photo, I'm at my birthday party. I'm twelve. I'm very happy. The party is at my house. My cake is big! My friends and family are here. My granny and grandad are here too. My granny is British and my grandad is Spanish.

My presents are cool. My favourite present is my mobile phone. It's blue. I'm in my new dress. It's my favourite colour: red.

1 Read the text. Complete the sentences with one word in each gap.

0 I'm *twelve* years old.
1 My ____________ is big.
2 My ____________ and family are at the party.
3 My grandad ____________ British.
4 My presents ____________ cool.
5 My favourite present is my ____________ mobile phone.
6 In the photo, I'm in my new red ____________.

Listening

2 2.4 Listen and write the correct answer.

0 Where's Uncle Tom? *B*

A 
B 
C 

1 What's Lily's favourite birthday present? ☐

A 
B 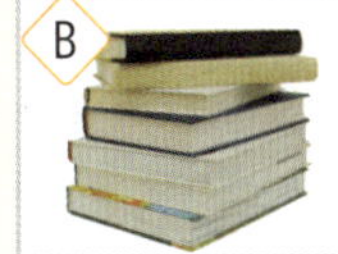
C 

2 What's in the bag? ☐

A 
B 
C 

3 How old is Joe? ☐

A 

B 12
C 

Vocabulary and Grammar

3 Complete the dialogues with one word in each gap.

Dialogue 1

Rita: Hi, I'm Rita. [0] *Are* you our new neighbour?
Leo: Yes, I [1] ____________ . My name's Leo.
Rita: This [2] ____________ my brother, Sam.
Leo: Hi, Sam.

Dialogue 2

Dylan: Are [3] ____________ your trainers, Sue?
Sue: [4] ____________ , they [5] ____________ . My trainers are grey.
Dylan: How about the backpack?
Sue: Yes, [6] ____________ is my backpack.

4 Choose the odd one out.

0 aunt (*uncle*) granny sister
1 at home on holiday in the box in the park
2 coat shoes jacket shirt
3 tracksuit skirt trainers T-shirt
4 mobile phone circle laptop mountain bike

Speaking

5 John is a new student in May's class. Match May's questions 0–4 with John's answers a–f. There is one extra answer.

0 *e* What's your name?
1 ☐ How old are you?
2 ☐ Where are you from?
3 ☐ What's your favourite sport?
4 ☐ Who's your favourite singer?

a It's football.
b Beyoncé.
c It's John.
d American.
e The UK.
f I'm thirteen.

YOUR SCORE

Reading and Writing:	__/6	Vocabulary and Grammar:	__/10
Listening:	__/3	Speaking:	__/4
		Total:	__/23

The lucky T-shirt

Cal's favourite thing in the world is music. He and his friends are in a band, Small Heroes. They are in a TV talent show. Today is the big final!

Mum: That T-shirt is too small for you, Cal.
Cal: It's my lucky T-shirt, Mum! It's always in my bag.

Mum: Good luck, darling! See you inside!
Cal: Thanks, Mum!

Damien: Oh, no! My guitar!
Ara: Ouch!
Evie: There are too many people out there! I'm scared!
Tony Right: Come on!
Cal: It's OK, guys! My lucky T-shirt is in my bag!

Before you read

1 Match sentences 1–4 with pictures A–D.

1 They're in a band. ☐
2 This is a talent show. ☐
3 He's scared. ☐
4 There are too many people in the picture. ☐

A

B

C

D

2 Look at the pictures on page 26. What do you think happens in the story?

While you read

3 RT1.1 Read and listen to the story. Then choose the correct answer.

1 What is Cal's band's name?
a Small Things
b Small Heroes
c TV Heroes

2 Cal's lucky T-shirt is
a old.
b new.
c big.

3 Who is not in the band?
a Ara
b Damien
c Tony

4 Cal is at the talent show, but where is his lucky T-shirt?
a It's in Cal's bag.
b It's at home.
c It's in the car.

After you read

4 What do the things below have in common?

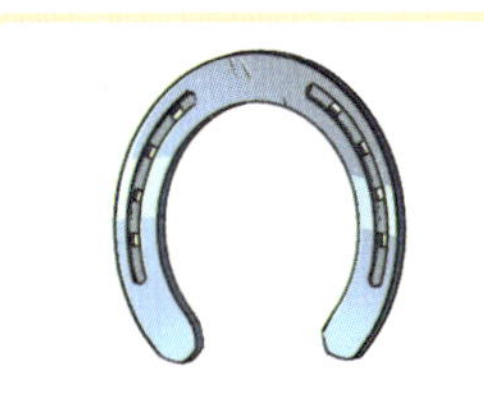

5 Match 1–6 with a–f to make phrases from the story. Check what they mean.

1 ☐ Good		a inside!
2 ☐ a talent		b final
3 ☐ the big		c a band
4 ☐ See you		d luck!
5 ☐ Come		e show
6 ☐ be in		f on!

6 RT1.2 How do you think the story ends for Small Heroes? Choose A or B. Then listen and check.

A ☐

They are the winners!

B ☐

They aren't the winners.

7 What do you think of the story? Colour the stars.

In the house

3

VOCABULARY
In the house | Prepositions of place | Household objects | Materials

GRAMMAR
there is/there are affirmative | *there is/there are* negative and questions

3.1 Vocabulary

In the house

1 Look at the pictures. Choose the correct option.

1 It's *a wall* / *a door.*
2 It's *an armchair* / *a bath.*
3 It's *a floor* / *a sofa.*
4 It's *a* bed / *a chair.*
5 It's *a desk* / *a table.*
6 It's *a fridge* / *a door.*
7 It's *a window* / *a wall.*

2 Complete the sentences with words from Exercise 1.

1 It's a *bath*.

2 It's a ________ .

3 It's a ________ .

3 Where are these things? Label the things with the words below.

bathroom bedroom garage garden ~~kitchen~~ living room

1 *kitchen*

2 ________

3 ________

4 ________

5 ________

6 ________

 I can talk about my house.

On the Portal
Extra Practice Activities: Lesson 3.1

Grammar

there is/there are affirmative

1 Choose the correct option. Then find the correct picture. Write *A* or *B*.

1 *There is / There are* an armchair. B
2 *There is / There are* five chairs. ☐
3 *There is / There are* a small picture. ☐
4 *There is / There are* a bed. ☐
5 *There is / There are* two sofas. ☐
6 *There is / There are* four windows. ☐

A

B

Vocabulary

2 Complete the sentences with the words below.

~~in~~ in next to on on under

1 Alex and Lian are *in* the living room.
2 There's a black table ________ the white table.
3 There's a mobile phone ________ the black table.
4 There are trainers ________ the table.
5 There's a chair ________ the living room.
6 There's a school bag ________ the chair.

3 Look and choose the correct option.

1 There *is / are* two girls *in / on* the garden.
2 There *is / are* two laptops *under / on* the table.
3 There *is / are* a bike *next to / on* the table.
4 There *is / are* two dogs *next to / under* the table.
5 There *is / are* a cat *on / in* the wall.
6 There *is / are* a book next *to / in* the school bag.

4 Complete the text with the words below.

a ~~are~~ are are in next on there

There [1] *are* blue walls [2] ________ my bedroom. There [3] ________ pictures [4] ________ the walls. There's [5] ________ small table [6] ________ to my bed. There [7] ________ some books on the table. [8] ________ is a laptop too.

5 Write four sentences about your bedroom. Use *in, on, next to, under* and the words below.

bed books box chair desk door photos window

1 ________________________________
2 ________________________________
3 ________________________________
4 ________________________________

I can use *there is/there are* and prepositions of place.

On the Portal
Extra Practice Activities: Lesson 3.2

3.3 Grammar

there is/there are negative and questions

1 Choose the correct option.

1 There *isn't* / *aren't* any chairs in the kitchen.
2 *Is* / *Are* there any laptops in the classroom?
3 *Is* / *Are* there a cat in the garden?
4 There *isn't* / *aren't* a TV in the living room.
5 *Is* / *Are* there a number on the door?
6 There *isn't* / *aren't* any people in the park.

2 Look at the picture and mark the sentences T (true) or F (false).

1 There isn't a table in the living room. T / F
2 There isn't a phone on the table. T / F
3 There aren't any pictures on the wall. T / F
4 There isn't a TV in the room. T / F
5 There aren't two tables in the room. T / F
6 There aren't any chairs in the room. T / F

3 Complete the sentences with *There isn't* or *There aren't*.

1 *There isn't* an armchair in the kitchen.
2 ________ any pictures on the wall.
3 ________ a bike in the garage.
4 ________ any sandwiches on the table.
5 ________ a mobile phone on my desk.
6 ________ any books in this bag.

4 Complete the questions with *Is there a* or *Are there any*.

1 *Is there a* laptop in the bedroom?
2 ________ photos on your laptop?
3 ________ cat under the bed?
4 ________ clothes in that bag?
5 ________ bike in the garage?
6 ________ pencils in the bag?

5 Match answers a–f with questions 1–6 in Exercise 4.

a ☐ No, there aren't. It's a new laptop.
b ☐ Yes, there are – my new jeans and a T-shirt.
c ☐ Yes, there is. There's a blue mountain bike.
d ☐ No, there aren't, but there are pens and a book.
e [1] Yes, there is. It's on the desk.
f ☐ No, there isn't, but there are two cats on my bed!

6 Write questions. Answer yes (✓) or no (✗). Use short answers.

1 trees / in your garden?
A: *Are there any trees in your garden?*
B: ✗ *No, there aren't.*

2 a garage / next to your house?
A: ________
B: ✗ ________

3 armchairs / in your living room?
A: ________
B: ✓ ________ Two armchairs and a sofa.

4 pencils / on your desk?
A: ________
B: ✗ ________ They're in my bag!

5 a desk / in your bedroom?
A: ________
B: ✓ ________ It's next to the window.

7 Complete the text with one word in each gap.

There [1] *are* a lot of things in the garage. There's [2] ________ old fridge and there [3] ________ two old armchairs. Are there [4] ________ bikes? No, there [5] ________ and there isn't [6] ________ car!

 I can use the negative and question forms of *there is/there are*.

On the Portal
Extra Practice Activities: Lesson 3.3

3.4 Speaking

Having a guest

1 3.1 Listen and repeat the phrases.

SPEAKING **Having a guest**

A: Hello. Please come in.
B: Thank you.
A: Would you like *a sandwich*?
B: Yes, please./No, thank you.
A: Where's the *bathroom*, please?
B: It's *next to the living room*. Let me show you.

2 Make dialogues.

a It's in the living room. Let me show you.
b Would you like a cake?
c Hi. Come in!
d Where's your laptop?
e Yes, please!
f Thanks.

3 Read the dialogues and choose TWO correct answers.

1 A: Where's the bathroom?
B: ___
(a) It's there.
(b) Let me show you.
c Yes, there is.

2 A: Would you like a cake?
B: ___
a No, thanks.
b Let me show you.
c Yes, please.

3 A: Where's my jacket?
B: ___
a Here it is.
b It's on the chair.
c Come in.

4 A: Please come in. Would you like a sandwich?
B: ___
a There's a sandwich.
b Yes, please.
c No, thanks.

5 A: Where's your bike?
B: ___
a No, it isn't.
b In the garden.
c At my friend's house.

4 Complete the dialogues with one word in each gap.

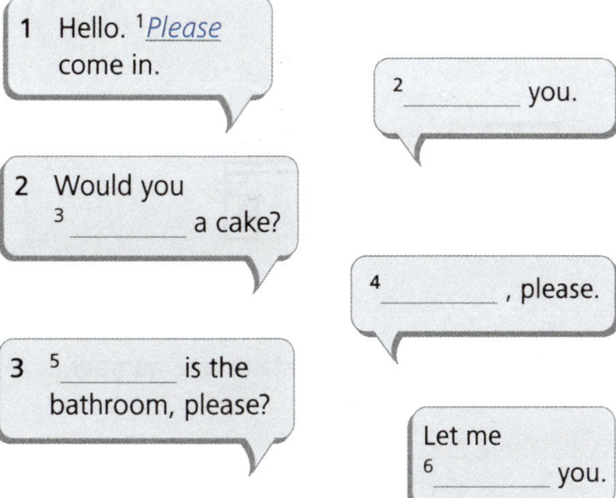

I can ask for something and ask where something is.

On the Portal
Extra Practice Activities: Lesson 3.4

Reading and Vocabulary

A holiday house

A house in a tree!

Luke is on holiday. Look! His holiday house is in a tree!

This tree house is very cool. There are two bedrooms: one is big and one is small. In the big bedroom there are two beds for me and my brother. The small bedroom is for my mum and dad.

There's a small kitchen and there's a big living room. There's a table in the kitchen and there are four chairs. In the living room there's a sofa. There isn't a television there.

1 What is there in the tree house? Read and tick (✓).

1 ☑

2 ☐

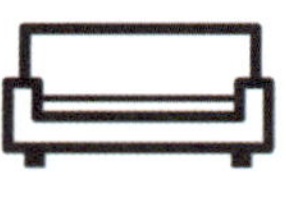

3 ☐

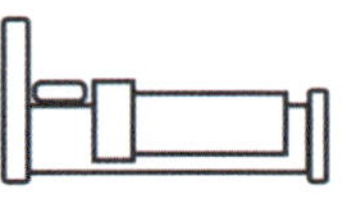

4 ☐

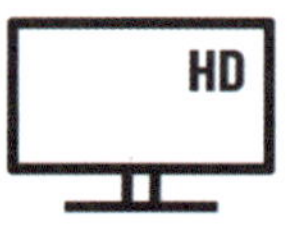

5 ☐

6 ☐

7 ☐

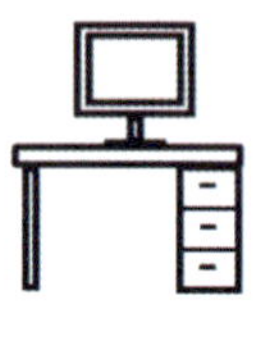

8 ☐

2 Complete the sentences with one number in each gap.

1 There are ______ rooms in the house.
2 There are ______ big rooms.
3 There are ______ people in Luke's family.

3 Look at the photos and do the puzzle.

 I can understand a text about a holiday house.

On the Portal
Extra Practice Activities: Lesson 3.5

3.6 Listening and Writing

Rooms in a house

1 3.2 **Listen to the dialogue. What is it about? Choose the correct answer.**

a Nancy's new house
b Nancy's bedroom
c Nancy's family

2 3.2 **Listen again. Correct the sentences.**

1 In Nancy's house there are two bedrooms.

____

2 There's a big kitchen.

____

3 There's a TV in Nancy's room.

____

3 3.2 **Listen again. Tick (✓) Nancy's house.**

A ☐

B ☐

C ☐

4 **Correct Jack's text. Add apostrophes.**

MY DREAM BEDROOM
by Jack

In my dream bedroom, there's a big bed. Its blue. Next to the bed, theres a table with a lamp. On the floor theres a big carpet. Its red, yellow and orange. Theres a computer and there are lots of posters and photos of my friends. There arent any plants in the room and there isnt a TV.

WRITING TIME

5 **Write about your dream bedroom. Use punctuation marks.**

1 Find ideas
Use the ideas below or your own ideas.

bed books carpet computer cushions desk fridge games console lamp posters sofa table TV

2 Draft
Give your text a title.
In my dream bedroom, there's ...
There isn't ...
There are/aren't ...

3 Check and write
Check your punctuation and write the final version of your text.

I can understand and write short texts describing a room.

On the Portal
Extra Practice Activities: Lesson 3.6

3.7 CLIL: Science

Materials

1 Match the letters to make words for materials. Then label the photos.

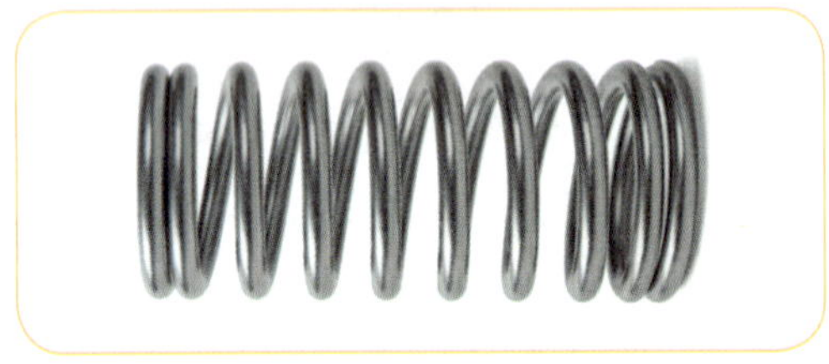

1 ______

2 ______

3 ______

4 ______

5 ______

2 Complete the sentences with the phrases below.

cardboard house glass walls ~~metal monster~~ paper lamp wooden chair

1 This *metal monster* is my brother's favourite thing!

2 Amy's house is very cool. There are ______ in the house!

3 Look at my cousins, Olivia and Mary! Olivia is in a recycled ______ . It's Olivia and Mary's favourite toy!

4 This ______ is in my granny's living room. It's very, very old and it's from China!

5 This blue and white ______ is next to my bed. It's my favourite thing.

3 Look at the picture. Then complete the sentences with the correct words.

1 The pages of the book aren't glass. They're p *a p e r*!

2 This isn't a cardboard chair. It's a m _ _ _ _ chair!

3 That isn't a wooden box. It's a g _ _ _ _ box!

4 This isn't a paper box. It's a c _ _ _ _ _ _ _ _ box!

5 Those aren't metal doors. They're w _ _ _ _ _ doors!

 I can talk and write about different materials.

My Language File

WORDLIST 3.3

In the house

bathroom (n) ______
bedroom (n) ______
door (n) ______
floor (n) ______
garage (n) ______
garden (n) ______
kitchen (n) ______
living room (n) ______
wall (n) ______
window (n) ______
armchair (n) ______
bath (n) ______
bed (n) ______
chair (n) ______
desk (n) ______
fridge (n) ______
sofa (n) ______
table (n) ______

Prepositions of place

in (prep) ______
next to (prep) ______
on (prep) ______
under (prep) ______

Household objects

carpet (n) ______
cushion (n) ______
lamp (n) ______
plant (n) ______
poster (n) ______
television (TV) (n) ______

Materials

cardboard (n) ______
glass (n) ______
metal (n) ______
paper (n) ______
wood/wooden (n, adj) ______

Extra words

another (determiner) ______
bad (adj) ______
car (n) ______
competition (n) ______
dream house ______
DVD (n) ______
go (v) ______
I'd like … ______
inside (adv) ______
milk (n) ______
naughty (adj) ______
Not really. ______
number (n) ______
orange juice (n) ______
parrot (n) ______
people (n) ______
perfect (n) ______
picture (n) ______
recycled (adj) ______
silly (adj) ______
skateboarder (n) ______

Sounds good!

Right here! ______
There it is! ______
Wait! ______
Yuck! ______

MY LANGUAGE NOTES

Self-check

Vocabulary

1 Look at the photos and the letters. Then write the words.

0 *lamp* 1 ________ 2 ________

3 ________ 4 ________ 5 ________

2 Look at the pictures. Choose the correct option.

The mouse is [0]*in* / *on* the [1]*bathroom / bedroom*. It's [2]*under / on* the desk.

This is the [3]*kitchen / living room*. The mouse is [4]*in / next to* the [5]*fridge / door*.

Grammar

3 Choose the correct option.

0 There *isn't* / *aren't* a cat in the garden.
1 There *is / are* three books on the desk.
2 There isn't *a pen / any pens* in my bag.
3 There *isn't / aren't* any chairs in the classroom.
4 There *is / are* a book on the desk.
5 There *are / aren't* any plants in the living room.

4 Complete the dialogues with one word in each gap.

1 A: [0]*Is* there a television in the kitchen?
B: No, there [1]________ .
2 A: [2]________ there [3]________ posters on the wall?
B: No, there [4]________ .
3 A: Is there [5]________ computer in your bedroom?
B: Yes, there is.

Speaking

5 Order the sentences to make a dialogue.

a ☐ It's in the living room. Let me show you.
b ☐ No, thank you. Where's your new television?
c ☐ Oh, wow! Cool!
d *0* Hi! Please come in.
e ☐ Thanks.
f ☐ Would you like a drink?

YOUR SCORE			
Vocabulary:	__/10	Speaking:	__/5
Grammar:	__/10	**Total:**	__/25

On the Portal
Extra Practice Activities: Self-check

BBC CULTURE

What do houses look like in the UK?

1 Look at the photos and complete the sentences with the words below.

cottage ~~detached~~ flats houseboat semi-detached terraced

1 This is a *detached* house.

2 These are ________ houses.

3 This is a ________ .

4 This is a ________ .

5 These are ________ houses.

6 This is a block of ________ .

2 Match 1–4 with a–d.

1 ☐ That's my house! It's small and the garden is small too. My house is in the country. There aren't lots of people here, but there are lots of trees and flowers.

2 ☐ My house is in a big city. My friend Jason's house is next to my house. And my friend Lisa's house is next to my house too!

3 ☐ My home isn't in the city. There aren't a lot of rooms, and the rooms are very small. There isn't a garden, but there's a lot of water!

4 ☐ My home is in the city. There isn't a garden, but the view from my bedroom window is fantastic! There are a lot of people in this block.

a My home is a terraced house.
b My home is a flat.
c My home is a cottage.
d My home is a houseboat.

VOCABULARY
Face, eyes, hair | Parts of the body | Personality adjectives | Adjectives

GRAMMAR
have got affirmative and negative | Regular and irregular plurals | *have got* questions and short answers | Possessive adjectives

About me 4

4.1 Vocabulary

Face, eyes, hair

1 Label the picture.

1 *ear* 3 ______ 5 ______
2 ______ 4 ______

2 Look at the pictures. Choose the correct option.

1 (short) / long
(blond) / red

2 straight / spiky
red / brown

3 curly / wavy
black / blond

4 short / long
dark / blond

3 Look and complete the sentences.

1 Jake's hair is s *h o r* t and s _ _ _ _ .

2 Lin's hair is l _ _ _ and s _ _ _ _ _ _ _ .

3 Diego's hair is c _ _ _ _ and b _ _ _ _ .

4 Martha's hair is w _ _ _ and b _ _ _ _ .

4 Look and complete the descriptions with the words below.

big ~~black~~ blond brown green grey ~~long~~ long short ~~small~~ small straight

1 *long*, wavy, *black* hair and *small*, blue eyes
2 short, ______, brown hair and big, ______ eyes
3 ______, curly, ______ hair and ______, ______ eyes
4 ______, straight, ______ hair and ______, blue eyes

5 Do these words describe eyes or hair? Write *E* (eyes) or *H* (hair).

1 wavy *H*
2 big ☐
3 blond ☐
4 straight ☐
5 short ☐
6 small ☐

 I can describe someone's face, eyes and hair.

On the Portal
Extra Practice Activities: Lesson 4.1

Grammar

have got affirmative and negative

1 Choose the correct option.

1 I *have* / *has* got two brothers.
2 My granny *have* / *has* got curly, white hair.
3 We *have* / *has* got a small car.
4 The students *have* / *has* got a very good teacher.
5 Ben *have* / *has* got big feet.
6 You *have* / *has* got very long hair.
7 My cat *have* / *has* got yellow eyes.
8 I *have* / *has* got brown eyes and brown hair.

2 Make sentences. Use the affirmative (✓) and negative (✗) form of the verb *have got*.

1 Alex / a new mobile phone ✓
Alex has got a new mobile phone.
2 he / a new skateboard ✗
______
3 Jen / a new coat ✗
______
4 she / a new skirt ✓
______
5 Alex and Jen / a cat ✗
______
6 they / a games console ✓
______

3 Match photos 1–4 with the parts of the body below.

arm feet fingers hands ~~head~~

1 *head*
2 ______

3 ______
4 ______ and ______

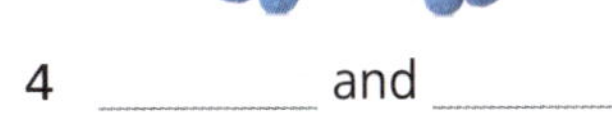

4 Complete the texts with plural nouns. Then match the texts with the photos.

A
a snake

B
a crocodile

1 ☐ I've got four short [1]*legs* (leg). My [2]______ (foot) are small. I've got two [3]______ (eye) and a big head.

2 ☐ I've got a long body. I haven't got any [4]______ (leg) or [5]______ (foot). I've got two [6]______ (eye). I haven't got any [7]______ (ear).

5 Complete the text with the affirmative (✓) and negative (✗) form of the verb *have got*.

Hi! My name is Ben. I'm twelve. I [1]*'ve got* (✓) two sisters. I [2]______ (✗) any brothers.
We [3]______ (✓) two pets – a rabbit and a cat. The cat's name is Softy, but the rabbit [4]______ (✗) a name.
My school is big. We [5]______ (✓) lots of teachers. I'm in class 7. My best friend's name is Zack. He [6]______ (✓) curly, brown hair and big ears!

I can use the affirmative and negative forms of the verb *have got*.

On the Portal
Extra Practice Activities: Lesson 4.2

4.3 Grammar

have got questions and short answers

1 Choose the correct option.

1 *Have* / *Has* X1 and X2 got big heads?
2 *Have* / *Has* I got super powers?
3 *Have* / *Has* Dug got a good friend?
4 *Have* / *Has* you got super ears?
5 *Have* / *Has* Kit got green eyes?
6 *Have* / *Has* Dug and Kit got super eyes?

2 Match answers a–f with questions 1–6 in Exercise 1.

a [ ] No, I haven't.
b [ ] No, you haven't.
c [ ] Yes, he has.
d [1] Yes, they have.
e [ ] No, they haven't.
f [ ] Yes, she has.

3 Make questions with the verb *have got*.

1 Have we got super powers?
2 ______ your classmates ______ super powers?
3 ______ your dad ______ a lot of friends?
4 ______ you ______ a sister?
5 ______ your granny ______ a computer?
6 ______ your parents ______ a new car?

4 Write true short answers for the questions in Exercise 3.

1 No, we haven't.
2 ______
3 ______
4 ______
5 ______
6 ______

5 Look and complete the sentences with *his, her, its, our, your* or *their*.

1 My brothers are young. Their bikes aren't fast.

2 This cat is small. ______ legs are short.

3 Grandad's got grey hair. ______ eyes are brown.

4 Well done, Noah and Lily! ______ homework is very good.

5 We've got a car. ______ car is big!

6 Julie's clothes are black and white. ______ skateboard is blue.

6 Look and complete the dialogues with the words below.

any got ~~has~~ have haven't his its their 've

A: [1]Has Jimmy [2]______ a dog?
B: Yes, he has. [3]______ dog has got short legs, but [4]______ ears are very long.

A: [5]______ you got [6]______ sisters?
B: Yes, I [7]______ got two sisters. [8]______ names are Lisa and Mariah. But I [9]______ got any brothers.

I can ask questions with the verb *have got* and use *his, her, its, our, your, their.*

On the Portal
Extra Practice Activities: Lesson 4.3

4.4 Speaking

Apologising

1 4.1 Listen and repeat the phrases.

SPEAKING Apologising

A: I'm so sorry.
Sorry about that!
Sorry, my mistake.

B: It's OK.
That's all right.
No problem.

2 Order the sentences to make dialogues.

1 a ☐ Are you sure?
b ☐ It's OK.
c ☐ *1* Oh no! I'm so sorry!
d ☐ Yes, it's all right.

2 a ☐ Oh, my mistake. Here you are.
b ☐ Thanks.
c ☐ Hey! That's my book!

3 a ☐ That's all right.
b ☐ Yes, no problem.
c ☐ Oops! Sorry!
d ☐ Are you sure?

3 Read the dialogues. Choose the correct answer.

1 A: I'm sorry.
B: (a) That's all right.
b Thank you.

2 A: Sorry about that!
B: a No problem.
b Are you sure?

3 A: Oh no! Look at that! I'm so sorry!
B: a Yes, I'm fine.
b It's OK.

4 A: Sorry, it's my mistake.
B: a Are you sure?
b That's all right.

5 A: Where's my book?
B: a Sorry, my mistake.
b Sorry, I've got it.

4 Complete the dialogues with one word in each gap.

1 A: I can't find my book!
B: I've got it! [1]*Sorry* about that.
A: [2]______ all right.

2 A: Oops! I'm so [3]______ !
B: It's OK.
A: Are you [4]______ ?
B: Yes, no [5]______ .

3 A: These aren't my keys.
B: Sorry, my [6]______ . Here you are.
C: It's [7]______ .

5 Look at the picture. Complete the dialogue.

Eddie: *Ram, that's my bag!*
Ram: ________________
Eddie: ________________

I can say sorry and respond to an apology.

On the Portal
Extra Practice Activities: Lesson 4.4

4.5 Reading and Vocabulary

My things, my family, my friends and I

Hi. My name's Tim. I'm twelve and I'm from London. I've got two brothers, three sisters and … ten cousins!

I've got a lot of books, a bike and a skateboard. I'm not good at sports, but my best friend is very good at football. His name is Max.

Max is my neighbour too. Our favourite place is his garden. We've got a little house in a tree! Max has got a sister. Her name is Lucy and she's very clever. Max and I aren't good at Maths, but Lucy is helpful. She's very nice!

1 Read the text. Tick (✓) the things Tim has got or does.

1 ☑

2 ☐

3 ☐

4 ☐

5 ☐

6 ☐

2 Read the text again. Mark the sentences T (true) or F (false).

1 Tim has got a big family. (T) / F

2 There are two boys in Tim's family. T / F

3 Tim has got a lot of books. T / F

4 Max has got a garden. T / F

5 Lucy is Tim's sister. T / F

3 Complete the sentences with the words below.

clever friendly funny ~~helpful~~

This is Rose. She's my granny. She's [1] *helpful*.

This is Damian. He's my cousin. He's very [2] ________.

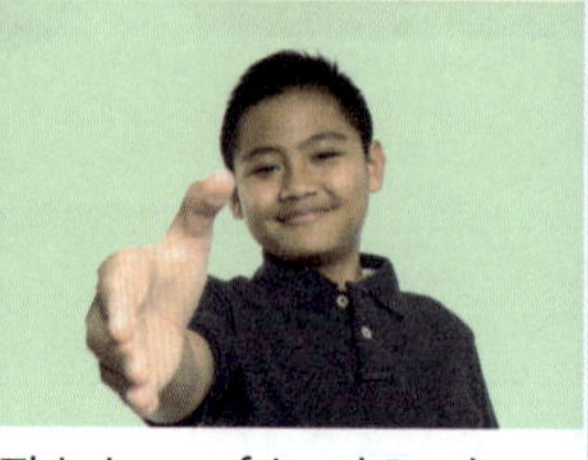

This is my friend Paul. He's [3] ________.

Sylvia is my sister. She's [4] ________.

 I can understand a text about a person, their things, family and friends.

On the Portal
Extra Practice Activities: Lesson 4.5

4.6 Listening and Writing

Animals

1 4.2 Listen and put the photos in the correct order. Write 1–3.

a panda ☐

a dolphin ☐

an ostrich ☐

2 4.2 Listen again. Tick (✓) for yes and put a cross (✗) for no.

	dolphins	pandas	ostriches
friendly	✓		
funny			
clever			

3 Read the text. Divide it into two paragraphs.

Elephants are very big! They've got big bodies, big ears and very long trunks. Elephants aren't very friendly. Sometimes they're helpful. They're clever too.

4 Choose the correct option.

Paragraph 1 / *Paragraph 2* is about elephants' personalities.

WRITING TIME

5 Write two paragraphs about tigers.

1 Find ideas

Use the words below and your own ideas.

Paragraph 1	big | yellow eyes | orange, black and white
Paragraph 2	clever (✓) | friendly (✗)

2 Draft

Write a paragraph describing the tiger's body.
Write a paragraph describing the tiger's personality.

3 Check and write

Check the paragraphs and write the final version of your text.

I can understand and write short texts about animals.

On the Portal
Extra Practice Activities: Lesson 4.6

CLIL: Science

Genes

1 Look at the pictures and do the puzzle. What is the mystery word?

1 He's ______.

2 He's ______.

3 They're ______.

4 They're the ______.

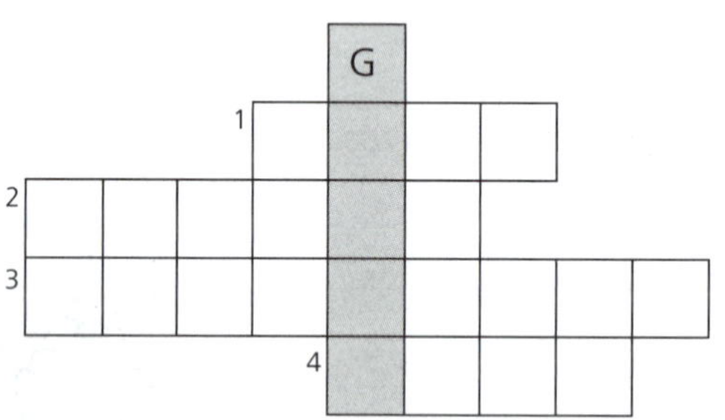

Mystery word: ______

2 Colour Fizzy, Filly and Fleeb's hair and eyes.

B	blue – strong
Y	yellow – strong
g	green – weak
r	red – weak

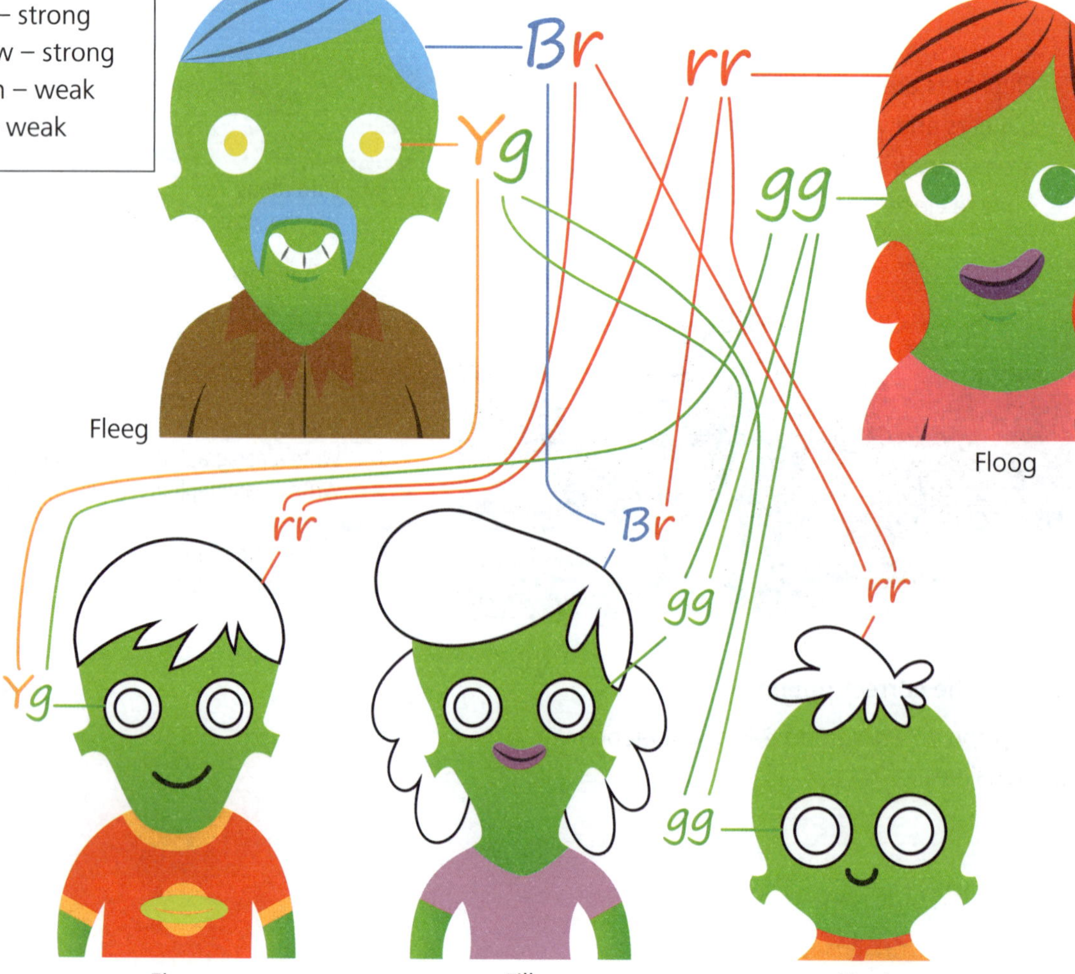

 I can understand gene combinations.

My Language File

WORDLIST 4.3

Face, eyes, hair

blond (adj) ____
blue (adj) ____
brown (adj) ____
curly (adj) ____
dark (adj) ____
ears (n) ____
eyes (n) ____
face (n) ____
green (adj) ____
grey (adj) ____
mouth (n) ____
nose (n) ____
red (adj) ____
spiky (adj) ____
straight (adj) ____
wavy (adj) ____

Parts of the body

arm (n) ____
body (n) ____
fingers (n) ____
foot (plural: feet) (n) ____
hand (n) ____
head (n) ____
leg (n) ____

Personality adjectives

clever (adj) ____
friendly (adj) ____
funny (adj) ____
helpful (adj) ____
nice (adj) ____

Adjectives

different (adj) ____
same (adj) ____
strong (adj) ____
weak (adj) ____

Extra words

a lot of (quantifier) ____
always (adv) ____
answer (n) ____
battery power ____
combination (n) ____
dancing (n) ____
do a quiz ____
fine (adj) ____
gene (n) ____
good at ____
good student ____
group (n) ____
high (adj) ____
home lover ____
homework (n) ____
house key ____
How many? ____
Hurry up! ____
joke (n) ____
like (prep) ____
long (adj) ____
Oh, dear! ____
Ouch! ____
party animal (n) ____
person (n) ____
personality (n) ____
place (n) ____
room (n) ____
say (v) ____
short (adj)
sometimes (adv) ____
speak (v) ____
subject (n) ____
super power (n) ____
sweetie (n) ____
tall (adj) ____
time (n) ____
usually (adv) ____
What kind of … ? ____

Sounds good!

Help me, please! ____
It isn't my fault! ____
Stop it! ____

MY LANGUAGE NOTES

Self-check

Vocabulary

1 Match the words below with the categories.

big ~~blond~~ helpful legs nose wavy

Hair: 0 *blond*, 1 ______
Eyes: 2 ______
Face: 3 ______
Body: 4 ______
Personality: 5 ______

2 Look at the pictures. Complete the phrases with the words below.

clever curly friendly ~~funny~~ long straight

0 very *funny* hair

1 very ______ legs

2 ______ hair

3 ______ red hair

4 nice and ______

5 very ______

Grammar

3 Complete the dialogues with *have, haven't, has, hasn't* or *got*.

1 A: Mark [0]*has* got brown eyes.
[1]______ he got brown hair too?
B: No. His hair is black. His parents and all his brothers have [2]______ black hair.

2 A: [3]______ you got a new bike?
B: No, I [4]______ . It's my old bike.

3 A: Ann [5]______ got any sisters, but she's got one brother.
B: Is he nice?

4 Complete the sentences with *his, her, its, your, our* or *their.*

0 Hello. What are *your* names, please?
1 I've got two cousins. ______ names are Clare and Joe.
2 Grandad's hair is grey and ______ eyes are blue.
3 I've got one sister. ______ name is Paula.
4 We're friends. ______ names are Kay and Dee.
5 That dog is big and ______ ears are very long!

Speaking

5 Complete the dialogues with the words and phrases below.

all right it's mistake problem ~~so sorry~~ sure

A: Hello, Danny.
B: My name isn't Danny. It's Tom.
A: Oh, I'm [0]*so sorry* !
B: No [1]______ !

A: Hey! You've got my bag!
B: Oops! My [2]______ ! Sorry.
A: That's [3]______ .

A: Ouch! Your bag is on my foot!
B: Sorry!
A: [4]______ OK.
A: Are you [5]______ ?

YOUR SCORE

Vocabulary:	__/10	Speaking:	__/5
Grammar:	__/10	**Total:**	**__/25**

On the Portal
Extra Practice Activities: Self-check

Quick Progress Check Units 1–4

Reading and Writing

Sunny's blog — My new band!

I'm in a band with Jake and Mick from my class. In the photo, they're in my garage!

Jake and Mick are very nice. Jake's twelve. He's got short dark hair and big brown eyes. He's tall. He's good at the guitar because he's got big hands and long fingers. Mick's thirteen. He's got curly hair and small, brown eyes. He's short. He's good at the guitar too. I haven't got a guitar – I'm the singer in our band.

Bye!

1 Read the text. Complete the sentences with one or two words in each gap.

0 There are *three* children in the band.
1 Jake's hair is short and ________ .
2 Jake's ________ are big.
3 Mick is ________ years old.
4 Mick's hair is ________ .
5 Mick and Jake can play ________ .

Vocabulary and Grammar

2 Choose the correct option.

We've got a new [0]*house / flat*! [1]*There / They* are two bedrooms. One bedroom is for my parents and one bedroom is for me and my sister. In [2]*our / its* bedroom, we've got two beds, two desks and two [3]*floors / chairs*. My bed is [4]*next to / in* the window. I've got my [5]*favourite / friendly* posters on my wall.

There's a living room and a big [6]*bathroom / kitchen*. It's got a table and four chairs. We've got a [7]*garage / garden*. It's got our car, our mountain bikes and an old fridge.

Listening

3 4.4 Listen and choose the correct option.

0 Anne has got a *computer game / skateboard*.
1 Charlie's computer is in *his bedroom / the kitchen*.
2 Charlie's dad is in the *garden / garage*.
3 Charlie's brother has got short, *curly / spiky* blond hair.
4 There's a cat next to the *brown / black and white* box.

Speaking

4 The Smith family are at Granny and Grandad's new house. Match pictures 1–4 with sentences a–e.

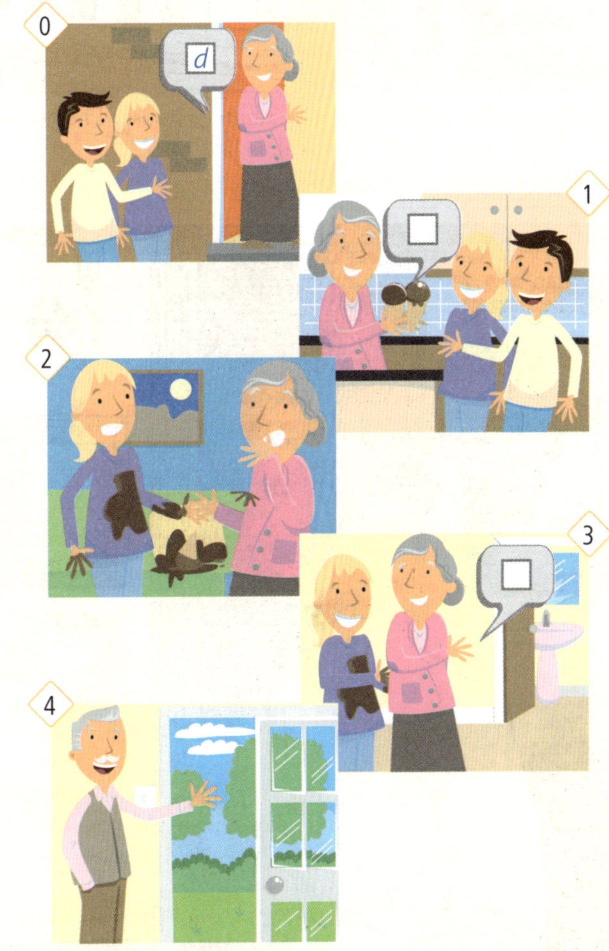

a Let me show you.
b Would you like an ice cream?
c I'm so sorry!
d Please come in.
e Look! There's a big garden!

YOUR SCORE

Reading and Writing:	__/5	Listening:	__/4
Vocabulary and Grammar:	__/7	Speaking:	__/4
		Total:	__/20

The painting

1
'Yellow Chair Under an Orange Tree'. My favourite painting! It's in Room 3.
Hi, Val! What? Oh, OK. Hurry up!
Artist
James
mson
The Early Paintings

Bisa loves art. She is in a famous painter's house. The house is now a museum. Her friend, Val, is late.

Bisa: There's the painting! But those two people … They're too close to the painting …

Val: Sorry I'm late. Is everything OK?
Bisa: Well, there's a man and a woman … They're in that room …
Val: And?
Bisa: Let me show you …

Bisa: Oh, no! Where's the painting?

Police officer: Tell me about the man and the woman.
Bisa: The man is short. He's got long, straight, blond hair. The woman is very tall. She's got short, curly, brown hair. They've got blue jeans, black jackets and trainers. His trainers are white and her trainers are red.

Before you read

1 Match sentences 1–4 with pictures A–D.

1 She is a famous painter. ☐
2 He is late. ☐
3 This is a ticket. ☐
4 She is too close to the TV. ☐

A

B

C

D

2 Look at the pictures on page 48. What do you think happens in the story?

While you read

3 RT2.1 Read and listen to the story. Mark the sentences T (true) or F (false).

1 Bisa is in a museum. T / F
2 There's an orange chair in Bisa's favourite painting. T / F
3 Val has got Bisa's ticket. T / F
4 The man and the woman are in Room 3. T / F

4 Help the police. Read the story on page 48 again. Then look at the pictures. Who are the man and the woman from the museum? Tick (✓) A or B.

A ☐

B ☐

After you read

5 What do the expressions in bold mean?

1 **Hurry up**, Mark!
2 That's **my favourite** painting!
3 **I'm late.**
4 **Is everything OK?**

6 Match expressions 1–4 in Exercise 5 with a–d to make dialogues.

a That's all right. ☐
b Yes, it is. ☐
c OK. ☐
d It's beautiful! ☐

7 What do you think of the story? Colour the stars.

Things I can do

5

VOCABULARY
Action verbs | *make, play, ride* | Language | Musical instruments

GRAMMAR
can affirmative and negative | *can* questions and short answers

5.1 Vocabulary

Action verbs

1 Match words 1–8 with A–H in the picture.

1 [E] jump
2 [ ] draw
3 [ ] fly
4 [ ] ride
5 [ ] run
6 [ ] dance
7 [ ] swim
8 [ ] read

2 Cross out two letters to find action verbs.

~~a~~	f	i	~~d~~	x

1 *fix*

a	e	c	t	m

2 ______

i	s	i	r	n	g

3 ______

c	o	r	o	a	k

4 ______

w	o	r	i	t	d	e

5 ______

3 Complete the sentences with the words below.

cook fix fly ~~read~~ ride write

1 *Read* the book.

2 ______ the kite.

3 ______ this, please.

4 ______ those.

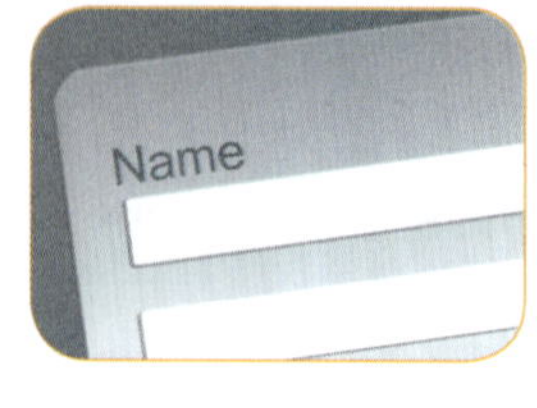

5 ______ your name, please.

6 ______ your bike.

 I can understand and use action verbs.

On the Portal
Extra Practice Activities: Lesson 5.1

5.2 Grammar

can affirmative and negative

1 Choose the correct option.

1 The girl (*can*) / *can't* read.
2 The man *can* / *can't* cook.
3 The cat *can* / *can't* write.

4 She *can* / *can't* run.
5 He *can* / *can't* fix a bike.
6 The bird *can* / *can't* fly.

2 Complete the sentences with *can* (✓) or *can't* (✗).

1 I *can* sing well. ✓
2 Sue ________ run fast. ✗
3 Grandad ________ play computer games. ✗
4 My mum ________ skateboard. ✓
5 Dad ________ cook very well. ✗
6 You ________ draw very good pictures. ✓
7 My sister ________ sing and dance. ✓
8 I ________ fix my bike. ✗

3 Make sentences with *can* (✓) or *can't* (✗).

1 Lian / draw animals ✓
Lian *can draw animals.*

2 Lucas / sing well ✗
Lucas ________________ .

3 Alex / fix computers ✓
Alex ________________ .

4 Granny / play the guitar ✗
Granny ________________ .

5 Jen / make cakes ✓
Jen ________________ .

4 Are sentences 1–6 true? Tick (✓) or put a cross (✗). Correct the false sentences.

1 Cats can't climb trees. ☒ *Cats can climb trees.*
2 Dogs can't jump. ☐ ________
3 I can fly. ☐ ________
4 Dogs can read. ☐ ________
5 My best friend can't cook. ☐ ________
6 I can't read Chinese. ☐ ________

5 Complete with *make*, *play* or *ride*. Tick (✓) the things you can do.

1 *play* football ☐
2 ________ a poster ☐
3 ________ a horse ☐
4 ________ a bike ☐
5 ________ the piano ☐
6 ________ cakes ☐

6 Complete the sentences with *can* or *can't* and the words below to make sentences that are true for you.

~~draw~~ fix make play run ride

1 I *can draw* pictures.
2 I ________ the guitar.
3 I ________ cakes.
4 I ________ computers.
5 I ________ a horse.
6 I ________ fast.

I can use the verb *can* in affirmative and negative sentences.

On the Portal
Extra Practice Activities: Lesson 5.2

5.3 Grammar

can questions and short answers

1 Read the sentences and write questions.

1 They can swim. *Can they swim?*
2 I can draw. ______
3 Tom can run fast. ______
4 May can sing well. ______
5 We can help. ______
6 The horse can jump. ______

2 Look at the picture. Answer the questions with the short answers below.

No, he can't. No, it can't. No, she can't.
No, they can't. Yes, he can. ~~Yes, they can.~~

1 Can Kit and Dug see the boat?
Yes, they can.
2 Can the boy and girl swim? ______
3 Can their mum swim? ______
4 Can Dug swim? ______
5 Can the small dog help? ______
6 Can Dug help? ______

3 Make questions with *can*.

1 you / fix a bike?
Can you fix a bike?
2 you / play football?
______
3 your mum / cook well?
______
4 your classmates / sing?
______
5 you / ride a horse?
______
6 your best friend / play the piano?
______

4 Answer the questions in Exercise 3 so that they are true for you. Use short answers.

1 ______
2 ______
3 ______
4 ______
5 ______
6 ______

5 Complete the dialogues with the correct form of the verb *can* and the verbs below.

dance help play see

1 A: [1]*Can* you [2]______ those red apples?
B: Yes, I [3]______ .
A: [4]______ you [5]______ me, please? I'm too short.
B: No problem.

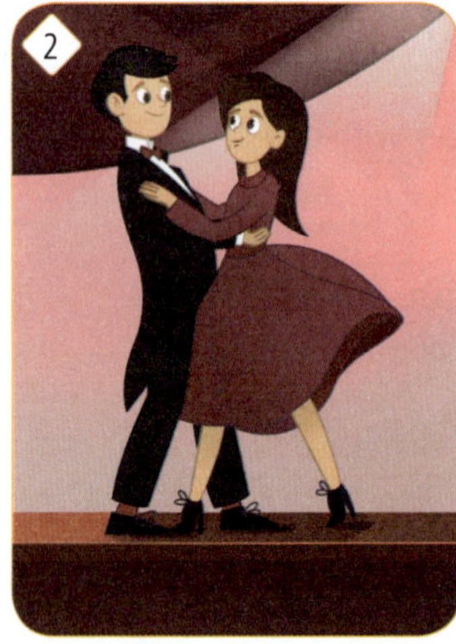

2 A: [6]______ they [7]______ ?
B: Yes, they [8]______ .
A: [9]______ the girl [10]______ the piano too?
B: No, she [11]______ .

 I can ask and answer questions with the verb *can*.

On the Portal
Extra Practice Activities: Lesson 5.3

5.4 Speaking

Suggestions

1 5.1 **Listen and repeat the phrases.**

SPEAKING Suggestions

A: Let's *do something fun*!
Let's *go ice skating*!
We can *go to the park*!

B: ☺ I agree!
Let's do that!
Great idea!
😐 I'm not sure.
☹ It's not a good idea.

2 Match the sentence halves.

1 [e] Let's play
2 [ ] We can swim
3 [ ] Let's have a party
4 [ ] Let's ride
5 [ ] We can go to
6 [ ] Let's make

a the park.
b for your birthday.
c chocolate cakes.
d our bikes.
e football after school.
f in the swimming pool.

3 Complete the phrases and draw a face.

1 Let's do *t h a t* ! ☺
2 It's not a _ _ _ _ idea.
3 Great _ _ _ _ !
4 I'm not _ _ _ _ .
5 I _ _ _ _ _ !

4 Complete the dialogue with the words below.

can haven't idea ~~Let's~~ play sure

A: Hi! [1]*Let's* play in the garden.
B: No, not the garden again. We [2]__________ go to the park.
A: Yes, great [3]__________ ! We can [4]__________ football.
B: I'm not [5]__________ .
A: Why not?
B: We [6]__________ got a ball.

I can make suggestions about what to do.

5 Choose the correct answer.

1 A: Let's watch TV.
B: Yes, I ______ .
(a) agree b 'm sure

2 A: Let's ______ to the park.
B: OK.
a go b can go

3 A: We can play a computer game.
B: ______
a Yes, I can. b Great idea!

4 A: Let's go swimming.
B: ______
a I'm sure. b That's not a good idea.

5 A: We ______ make sandwiches.
B: Let's do that.
a can b can't

6 Write suggestions and replies.

1 play a game ☺
A: *We can play a game!*
B: __________

2 make sandwiches 😐
A: __________
B: __________

3 go there ☹
A: __________
B: __________

On the Portal
Extra Practice Activities: Lesson 5.4

5.5 Reading and Vocabulary

A special dog

This is twelve-year-old Jasmine. She's with her best friend. Her best friend can't speak to Jasmine. He can't speak any languages! He isn't a boy and he isn't a girl. He's a special dog and his name is Henry.

Jasmine can't hear. She can't hear her friends, she can't hear music and she can't hear cars. But Jasmine is OK. She's got Henry, and Henry is her ears! Henry is a special 'hearing dog' and he can help Jasmine a lot! He can help her walk to school and to the park.

1 Read the text and choose the best title.

a A dog helps a girl
b A girl helps her dog
c Henry has got a problem

2 Read the text again. Choose the correct option.

1 Jasmine is *eleven* / *twelve* years old.
2 Jasmine's best friend *is* / *isn't* a boy.
3 *Henry* / *Jasmine* is a special dog.
4 Jasmine *has got some* / *hasn't got any* friends.
5 Jasmine *can* / *can't* hear cars.

3 Read the text again. Match 1–5 with a–e.

1 [c] Henry is Jasmine's
2 [ ] Henry can
3 [ ] Jasmine's best friend
4 [ ] Jasmine can't
5 [ ] Jasmine can

a help Jasmine.
b hear her friends.
c ears.
d is a dog.
e go to the park with Henry.

4 Look at the pictures and complete the sentences.

1 You can see people with your e _ _ s.

2 You can hear music with your e _ _ s.

3 You can smell flowers with your n _ _ e.

5 Complete the dialogue with the words below.

~~hear~~ learn sign language speak special

A: Look at these people. They can't [1] *hear* .
B: Can they [2] ________ English?
A: No, they can't, but they can speak a [3] ________ language.
B: Can I [4] ________ this language?
A: Yes, you can. I can teach you. It's [5] ________ and you make words with your hands.

On the Portal
Extra Practice Activities: Lesson 5.5

 I can understand a text about a special dog.

5.6 Listening and Writing

After-school clubs

1 What's this? Write the letters in the correct order.

2 5.2 Listen and choose the correct option.

At this club you can *make a new teddy bear / fix an old teddy bear.*

3 5.2 Listen again. Which is the correct teddy bear? Tick (✓).

A ☐

B ☐

C ☐

4 5.2 Listen again. Choose the correct option.

1 What is the girl's name?
Her name is *Sarah / Erin.*

2 Is the teddy bear Tommy's or his sister's?
It's *Tommy's / his sister's.*

3 Can Sarah fix it?
Yes, she can. / No, she can't.

4 What colour are the new eyes?
They're black. / They're blue.

5 Complete the blog post with *and* or *but*.

Come to our new Fix It Club!

It's fun [1]*and* it's free!
We can fix clothes [2]________ bikes. We can fix computers, [3]________ we can't fix cars. Sorry! You can watch us [4]________ you can learn to fix things too. We are at the Youth Club every Saturday morning, [5]________ not in the afternoon.

Come and visit us soon!

WRITING TIME

6 Write a blog post about the basketball club.

1 Find ideas
Use the notes below.

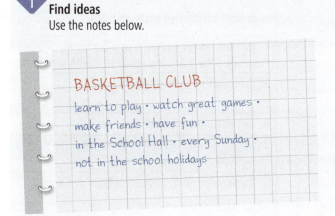

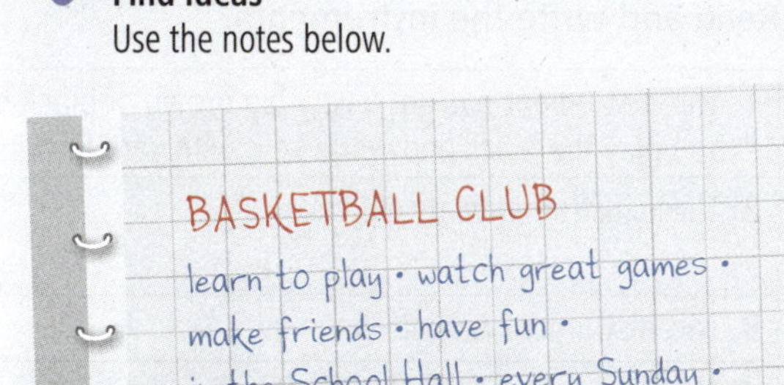

BASKETBALL CLUB
learn to play • watch great games •
make friends • have fun •
in the School Hall • every Sunday •
not in the school holidays

2 Draft

1 Write the title.
Come to our new BASKETBALL CLUB!

2 Write a paragraph about what you can do at the club.
You can … and …

3 Write where and when the club is.
Where: … When: …

4 Write the end.
See you there!

3 Check and write
Check the linkers (*and, but*) and write the final version of your text.

I can understand and write short texts about after-school clubs.

On the Portal
Extra Practice Activities: Lesson 5.6

CLIL: Music

Musical instruments

1 Look at the photos and do the puzzle.

Across

1

3

4

5

6

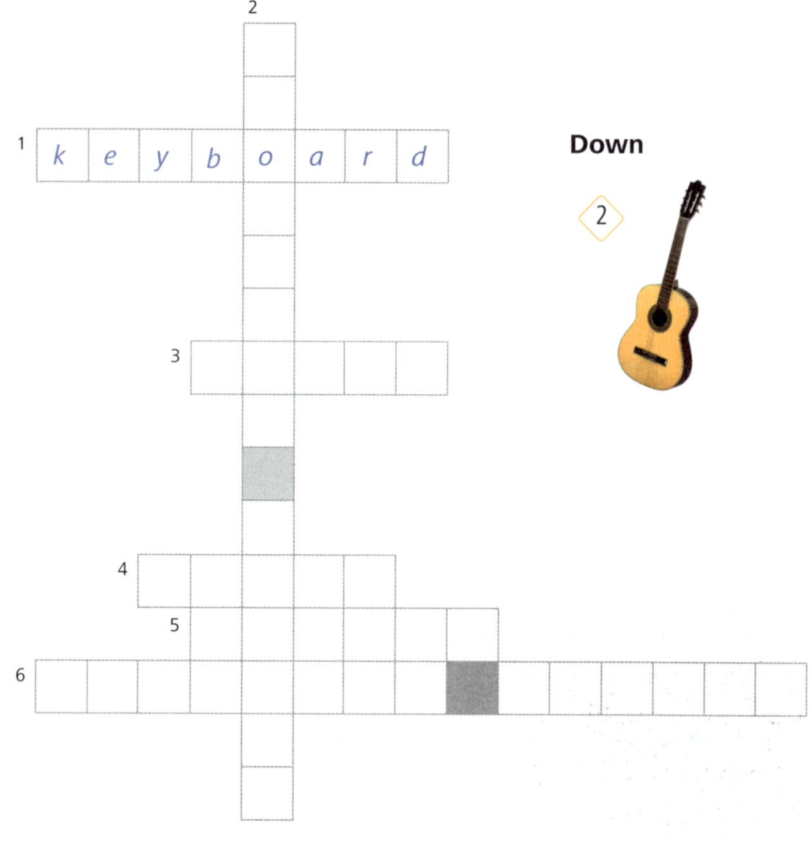

2 Read and write the instruments.

1 This instrument has got a very big brown or black body. You play the black and white keys with your fingers.	*piano*
2 These instruments are electric.	______ ______
3 This instrument is Spanish.	______
4 This instrument isn't very big. You play the black and white keys with your fingers.	______
5 These instruments have got a body and a neck.	______ ______ ______
6 This wooden instrument is small.	______
7 When you play this instrument, its body is on your legs.	______
8 You play this instrument with your feet and your hands.	______

3 What instruments can the people play? Do the puzzle and find the answers.

1 Alice can play the *drums*.
C2 + B2 + D5

2 Martin can play the ______ .
A3 + D4

3 Becky can play the ______ .
A4 + D2 + B3 + D1 + C1 + B4 + C5

4 Richard can play the ______ .
B1 + C4 + A1 + B5 + D3

5 Millie can play the ______ .
B5 + A5 + A2 + C3 + C1 + B4 + C5

	A	B	C	D
1	BO	K	GU	IC
2	S	U	DR	ECT
3	VIO	R	TIC	RD
4	EL	I	EY	LIN
5	COU	A	TAR	MS

 I can name and describe musical instruments.

My Language File

WORDLIST 5.3

Action verbs

act (v)
cook (v)
dance (v)
draw (v)
fix (v)
fly (v)
jump (v)
read (v)
ride (v)
run (v)
sing (v)
swim (v)
write (v)

make, play, ride

make cupcakes
make a poster
play computer games
play football
play the piano
ride a bike
ride a horse

Language

hear (v)
language (n)
learn (v)
sign language (n)
speak (v)
special (adj)

Musical instruments

acoustic guitar (n)
drums (n)
electric guitar (n)
keyboard (n)
violin (n)

Extra words

after-school (adj)
all day
boat (n)
camera (n)
club (n)
come (v)
fast (adv)
football (n)
game (n)
guys (n)
I can't see a thing.
important (adj)
letter (n)
lovely day
One minute, please.
star (n)
teach (v)
teacher (n)
video (n)
volleyball (n)
wear (v)
well (adv)
who (pronoun)
word (n)

Sounds good!

Let me see …
Not again!
What's wrong?

MY LANGUAGE NOTES

Self-check

Vocabulary

1 What can they do? Look and write the action verbs.

0 *fly*

1 ________

2 ________

3 ________

4 ________

5 ________

2 Choose the correct option.

0 *(draw)* / *read* a picture
1 *play* / *ride* the guitar
2 *play* / *make* a cake
3 *sing* / *read* a book
4 *ride* / *act* a bike
5 *sing* / *play* computer games

Grammar

3 Look at the table. Complete the sentences with *can* or *can't* and *and* or *but*.

	swim	run fast	fix a bike
Anna	✓	✓	✗
Tom	✗	✓	✓
Sam and Joe	✓	✓	✗

Anna can swim [0]*and* she [00]*can* run fast. Tom [1]________ run fast [2]________ he can fix a bike. Sam and Joe can swim, [3]________ they [4]________ fix a bike. Tom and Anna [5]________ run fast.

4 Look at the picture. Write questions and short answers. Answer yes (✓) or no (✗). Use the correct form of the verb *can*.

1 she / play the piano?
A: [0]*Can she play the piano?*
B: ✓ [1]________
2 the dogs / sing?
A: [2]________
B: ✗ [3]________
3 the boy / ride his bike?
A: [4]________
B: ✓ [5]________

Speaking

5 Complete the dialogue with one word in each gap.

Amy: [0]*Let's* do something.
Jack: OK. We [1]________ make a chocolate cake!
Amy: I'm not [2]________ . I [3]________ cook very well.
Jack: No [4]________ . I can teach you.
Amy: OK, cool. [5]________ idea!

YOUR SCORE

Vocabulary:	__/10	Speaking:	__/5
Grammar:	__/10	**Total:**	**__/25**

On the Portal
Extra Practice Activities: Self-check

BBC CULTURE

Young London

1 **Label photos 1–4 with the names below.**

Hyde Park the London Eye the Natural History Museum the Thames

1 ____________

2 ____________

3 ____________

4 ____________

2 **Match the letters to make six words. Then label photos 1–6.**

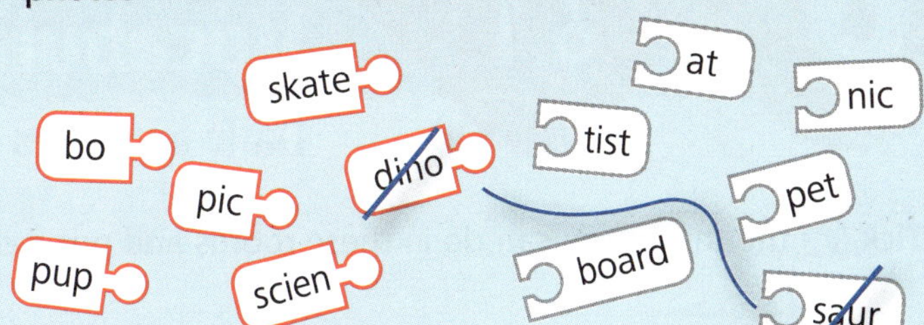

1 *dinosaur*

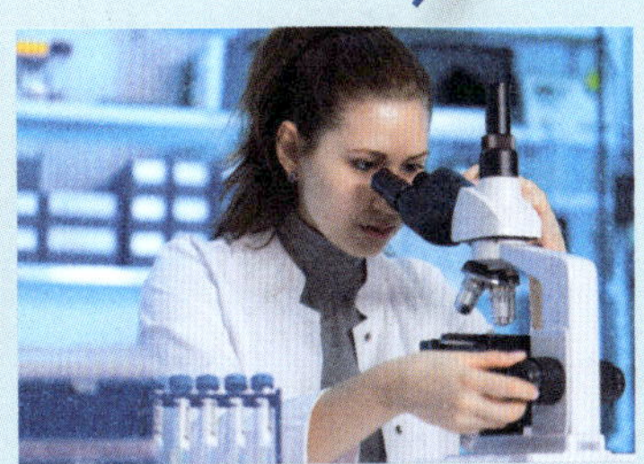

2 ____________

3 ____________

4 ____________

5 ____________

6 ____________

3 **Match sentences 1–8 with places a–e. You can use places a–e more than once.**

1 It's next to the Thames. *b*
2 You can be a scientist for a day there. ☐
3 You can draw funny people there. ☐
4 You can make your own comic book there. ☐
5 You can play football and skateboard there. ☐
6 You can see dinosaurs there. ☐
7 You can see London from the top. ☐
8 You can see London from a boat from there. ☐

a the Thames
b the London Eye
c Hyde Park
d the Natural History Museum
e the Cartoon Museum

My day 6

VOCABULARY
Daily activities | Days of the week | Months | On the internet

GRAMMAR
Present Simple affirmative | Adverbs of frequency

6.1 Vocabulary

Daily activities

1 Tick (✓) the things you can do in these rooms and put a cross (✗) for the the things you can't do.

1
- ☑ tidy my room
- ☐ have a shower
- ☐ listen to music
- ☐ do my homework
- ☐ hang out with my friends

2
- ☐ have lessons
- ☐ have lunch
- ☐ watch TV
- ☐ get up
- ☐ have breakfast

2 Find eight words. Then complete the phrases.

F	D	R	R	E	W	O	R	Y	T	C	S
R	I	H	O	M	E	W	O	R	K	A	H
I	N	O	L	U	Y	F	O	P	P	O	O
E	N	T	V	S	G	E	M	X	I	W	W
N	E	E	Q	I	E	C	K	D	S	S	E
D	R	R	S	C	H	O	O	L	O	M	R

1 do my *homework*
2 tidy my ________
3 have ________
4 have a ________
5 listen to ________
6 go to ________
7 watch ________
8 hang out with my ________

3 Complete the sentences with the words below.

do get up go go ~~have~~ have

1 I *have* lessons.
2 I ________ in the morning.
3 I ________ my homework.
4 I ________ to bed.
5 I ________ to school.
6 I ________ breakfast.

4 Write the sentences in Exercise 3 in the order you do them on a typical day.

6 ________
5 ________
4 *I have lessons.*
3 ________
2 ________
1 ________

 I can talk about daily activities.

On the Portal
Extra Practice Activities: Lesson 6.1

6.2 Grammar

Present Simple affirmative

1 Choose the correct option.

1 Jen *watch* / *watches* TV after dinner.
2 Alex *do* / *does* his homework in his room.
3 Lucas and Alex *play* / *plays* football in the park.
4 Jen and Alex *get* / *gets* up late.
5 Lucas's mum *listen* / *listens* to music in the kitchen.
6 Lucas *go* / *goes* to school with Jen and Alex.

2 Complete the table.

I/you/we/they	he/she/it
play	1 *plays*
2 ______	does
draw	3 ______
4 ______	drinks
5 ______	looks
wash	6 ______
carry	7 ______
8 ______	makes

3 Write sentences about Sam.

1 I have breakfast at seven o'clock.
Sam has breakfast at seven o'clock.

2 I go to school with my sister.
______

3 I do my homework before dinner.
______

4 I watch TV after dinner.
______

5 I play football with my friends.
______

6 I tidy my bedroom every weekend.
______

7 I visit my grandparents.
______

4 Complete the sentences with the Present Simple form of the verb in brackets.

1 My brother and I *like* (like) orange juice, but my sister ______ (drink) milk.
2 Mum and Dad ______ (watch) TV and my sister and I ______ (play) computer games after dinner.
3 Rob ______ (tidy) his room and he ______ (help) in the kitchen too.
4 Sue ______ (have) sandwiches for lunch. She ______ (eat) them in the classroom.
5 I ______ (hang out) with my friends after school. Then I ______ (have) dinner.
6 Harry ______ (do) his homework and then he ______ (watch) TV.

5 Complete the table. Write sentences about Laura and sentences that are true for you.

	Laura	Me
1 have lunch	SCHOOL	______
2 do homework		______
3 play		______
4 like		______

1 Laura *has lunch at school*.
I ______.
2 Laura ______.
I ______.
3 Laura ______.
I ______.
4 Laura ______.
I ______.

I can use the Present Simple in affirmative sentences.

On the Portal
Extra Practice Activities: Lesson 6.2

6.3 Grammar

Adverbs of frequency

1 Complete the sentences with adverbs of frequency.

1 Jack ■□□□ *sometimes* cycles to school.
2 Emma ■■■■ ______ has breakfast at home.
3 Pete ■■■□ ______ does his homework in his bedroom.
4 I ■□□□ ______ play in the park.
5 We □□□□ ______ watch TV in the morning.
6 My parents ■■□□ ______ go out with their friends.

2 Rewrite the sentences with the adverb in the correct place.

1 I'm busy on Saturday. (often)
I'm often busy on Saturday.
2 Kit helps me at home. (often)
______
3 Uncle Roberto visits me. (sometimes)
______
4 I cook dinner. (never)
______
5 Kit is happy. (always)
______
6 Kit and I have fun. (usually)
______

3 Complete the days of week. Then number them in the correct order.

4 Read the information about Tom and write sentences.

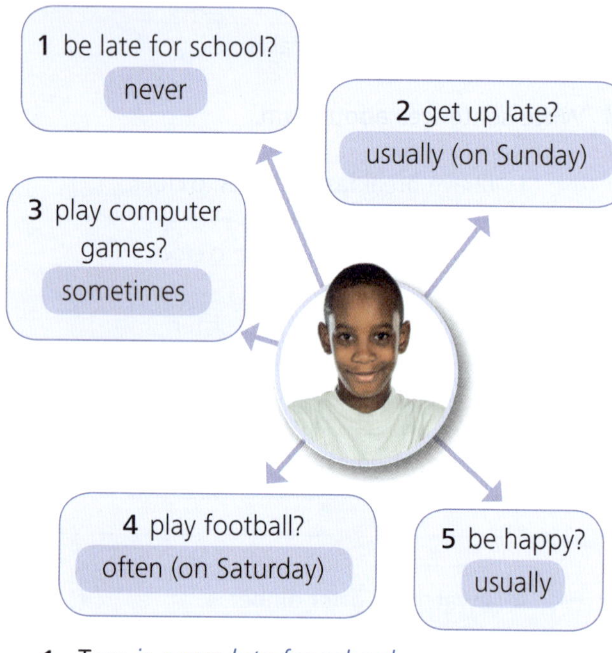

1 Tom *is never late for school*.
2 He ______.
3 He ______.
4 He ______.
5 He ______.

5 Now write sentences that are true for you. Use adverbs of frequency.

1 I ______ late for school.
2 ______
3 ______
4 ______
5 ______

I can use adverbs of frequency.

On the Portal
Extra Practice Activities: Lesson 6.3

Speaking

Telling the time

1 🔊 6.1 Listen and repeat the phrases.

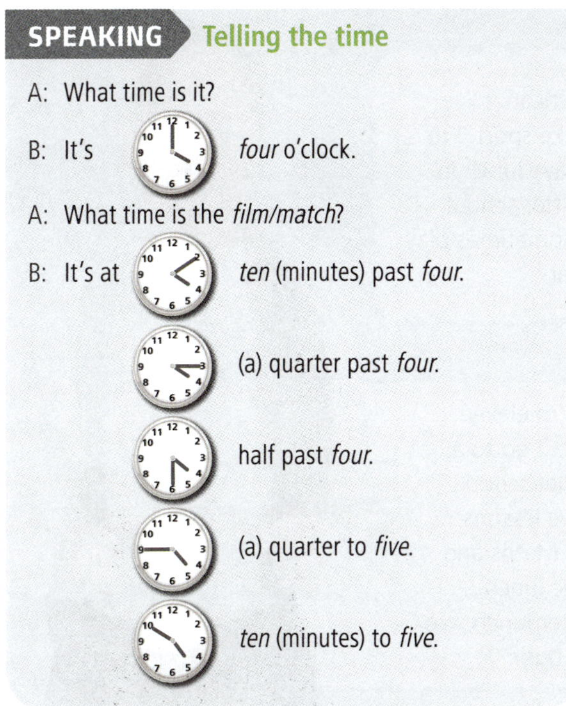

SPEAKING Telling the time

A: What time is it?

B: It's *four* o'clock.

A: What time is the *film/match*?

B: It's at *ten* (minutes) past *four.*

(a) quarter past *four.*

half past *four.*

(a) quarter to *five.*

ten (minutes) to *five.*

2 Match clocks a–h with phrases 1–8.

a 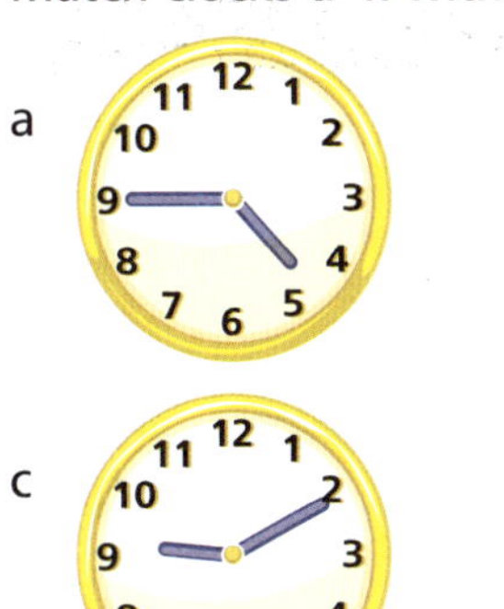

b 

c 

d 

e 

f 

g 

h 

1 [*b*] six o'clock
2 [ ] (a) quarter to five
3 [ ] half past two
4 [ ] five to one
5 [ ] (a) quarter past one
6 [ ] five past five
7 [ ] twenty to nine
8 [ ] ten past nine

I can tell the time.

3 Complete the sequences.

1 twelve o'clock – five past twelve – [1]*ten past twelve* – quarter past twelve – [2]________ – twenty-five past twelve – [3]________

2 half past two – [4]________ – twenty to three – [5]________ – ten to three – [6]________ – three o'clock

4 Look at the TV schedule. Then complete the questions and answers.

18:00	18:35	19:05	19:15	19:50
Pet Time	Super Girl	Happy Days	That's Magic	The Great Big Talent Show

1 A: What time is *Pet Time*?
B: *It's at six o'clock.*

2 A: What time is *That's Magic*?
B: ________

3 A: ________?
B: It's at five past seven.

4 A: ________?
B: It's at twenty-five to seven.

5 A: What time is *The Great Big Talent Show*?
B: ________

6 A: OK. ________ now?
B: It's five to six. Hurry up!

5 Order the sentences to make a dialogue.

a [*1*] What time is it, Mandy?
b [ ] No, I'm not. I'm late for my music lesson.
c [ ] It's at quarter to six. Bye!
d [ ] It's half past five. Oh, no!
e [ ] What's wrong? Are you OK?
f [ ] Oh, dear. What time is your music lesson?

6 Complete the sentences so they are true for you.

1 I get up at ________ .
2 I have breakfast at ________ .
3 I go to school at ________ .
4 I do my homework at ________ .
5 I go to bed at ________ .

On the Portal
Extra Practice Activities: Lesson 6.4

Reading and Vocabulary

Daily routines

Hi. I'm Mike. I'm twelve and I'm American. I live in New York. My school is very big. I like sport. I'm not very good at Art, but I love it. I have lunch in the classroom. I usually have pizza! After school, I always hang out with my friends. We sometimes play basketball or we go to the park.

My name is Eloise and I'm eleven. I'm from Paris, in France. I go to a special school. It's a ballet school! After breakfast, we have lessons. My favourite lessons are Maths and English. Then we have lunch. I often have pancakes! After lunch, we dance. I'm always busy.

1 Read the texts. Match photos A–F with Mike or Eloise.

1 Mike *B* ☐ ☐
2 Eloise ☐ ☐ ☐

A

B

C

D

E

F

2 Read the texts again. Mark the sentences T (true) or F (false).

1 Mike likes Art. (T) / F
2 He eats pizza in the classroom. T / F
3 He never goes to the park after school. T / F
4 Eloise likes Maths. T / F
5 She has pancakes every day. T / F
6 She dances before lunch. T / F

3 Read the texts again. Complete the sentences with one or two words in each gap.

1 Mike goes to a ________ school.
2 He plays basketball with ________ .
3 Eloise ________ after breakfast.
4 She is always ________ .

4 Complete the months.

1 D *e* c *e* *m* b *e* r
2 F e _ r _ a _ y
3 J _ n _
4 O _ _ o _ e r
5 A _ r _ l
6 A _ g _ _ t

5 Complete the sequence with the months in Exercise 4.

January | 1 ________ | March | 2 ________ | May | 3 ________ | July | 4 ________ | September | 5 ________ | November | 6 *December*

 I can understand texts about teenagers' daily routines.

On the Portal
Extra Practice Activities: Lesson 6.5

6.6 Listening and Writing

A typical weekend

1 🔊 6.2 **Listen to Andy and complete the notes.**

Andy's holidays

Country:	1 *Spain*
Aunt's nationality:	2 ______
Aunt's job:	3 ______
Favourite place:	4 ______
Favourite game:	5 ______

2 🔊 6.2 **Listen again. Choose the correct option.**

1 Andy (*always*) / *usually* goes on holiday in August.
2 After breakfast, they *usually* / *often* go to the beach.
3 They *always* / *often* have a picnic.
4 They *usually* / *often* go to bed after lunch.
5 Andy *always* / *never* gets up early.

3 Find *before* and *after* in Jane's blog post.

We never go to school in August. It's a holiday! I get up late. I often play computer games (before) breakfast. I never have breakfast in bed. I have it in the kitchen. After breakfast, I often hang out with friends. Before dinner, I sometimes help my parents. I usually watch TV after dinner. I often go to bed late.

4 Read Jane's blog post in Exercise 3 again. Put the activities below in the correct order.

~~get up~~ hang out with friends have breakfast play computer games

Before lunch

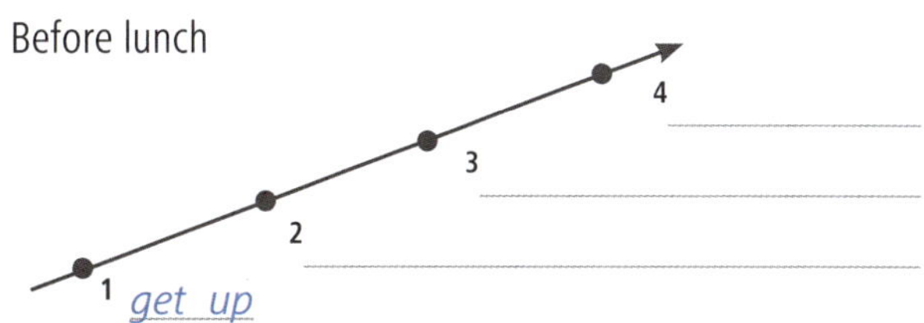

go to bed have dinner help my parents watch TV

After lunch

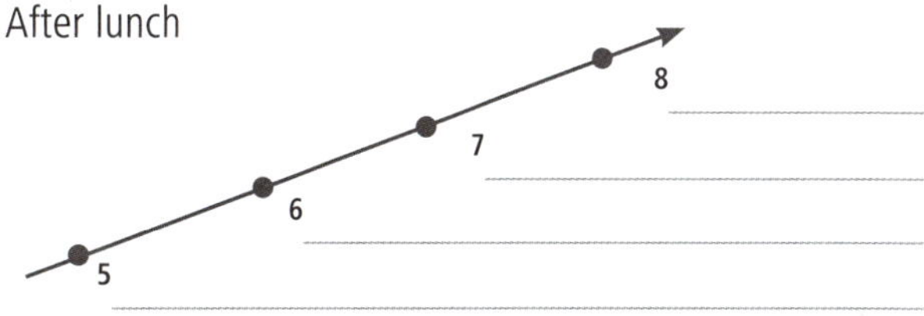

WRITING TIME

5 Write about your typical day on holiday. Use *before* and *after*.

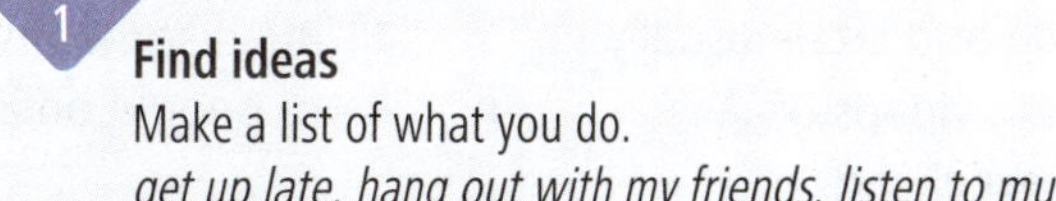

1 **Find ideas**
Make a list of what you do.
get up late, hang out with my friends, listen to music ...

2 **Draft**
Write a paragraph about your typical holiday day.
I usually get up at ...
I have a shower and I have breakfast.
After breakfast, I ...
I always ... Before lunch, I ...

3 **Check and write**
Check *before* and *after* and write the final version of your text.

I can understand and write short texts about a typical day on holiday.

On the Portal
Extra Practice Activities: Lesson 6.6

6.7 CLIL: Technology

The internet

1 Match 1–6 with a–f.

2 Look at the pictures and complete the sentences.

1 My cousin lives in the USA. We often have a v *i d e o* call at the weekend.

2 Danny loves his granny. He e _ _ _ _ _ her every week.

3 Linda and Lizzie usually watch videos o _ _ _ _ _ at the weekend.

4 Brian sometimes c _ _ _ _ to people online.

5 Angela sometimes g _ _ _ help with her homework.

6 Roger often reads this b _ _ _ . It's very interesting!

3 Complete the dialogues. Use sentences a–f below.

a Do you chat online?
b Yes, I often get help with my homework online.
c No, they don't! They text them.
d ~~On Saturday. We can have a video call.~~
e Do all his friends read it?
f No, I never watch it, but I often watch videos online.

1 A: When can I see you again?
B: *d*

2 A: Do you watch TV a lot?
B: ☐

3 A: Tom writes his blog every day. It's very funny!
B: ☐

4 A: My best friends don't live in the UK, but we chat every day.
B: ☐

5 A: Do young people often email their friends?
B: ☐

6 A: Do you need the internet for your school work?
B: ☐

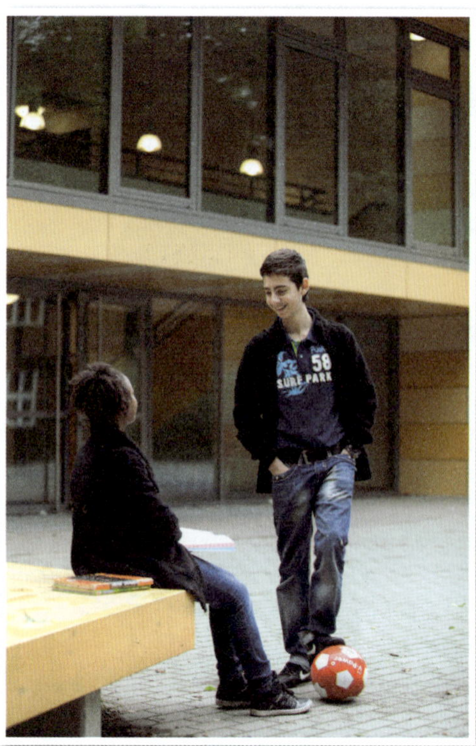

 I can describe things I can do on the internet.

My Language File

WORDLIST 6.3

Daily activities

do my homework
get up (v)
go to bed
go to school
hang out with my friends
have a shower
have breakfast
have dinner
have lessons
have lunch
listen to music
tidy my room
watch TV

Days of the week

Monday (n)
Tuesday (n)
Wednesday (n)
Thursday (n)
Friday (n)
Saturday (n)
Sunday (n)

Months

January (n)
February (n)
March (n)
April (n)
May (n)
June (n)
July (n)
August (n)
September (n)
October (n)
November (n)
December (n)

On the internet

chat online
email someone
get help with homework
have a video call
read/write a blog
watch videos online

Extra words

animal (n)
busy (adj)
busy week
cartoon (n)
classical music (n)
daily routine
early (adv)
every (determiner)
free day
get ready
grandparent (n)
gym (n)
hour (n)
How about … ?
in the evening
late (adv)
lesson (n)
life (n)
live (v)
love (v)
meet (v)
mess (n)
never (adv)
often (adv)
online (adv)
pancake (n)
really (adv)
school survey
swimming (n)
team (n)
teenager (n)
That's better.
The film is on again at …
too late
travel (v)
visit (v)
walk (v)
walking (n)
weekday (n)
writing (n)

Sounds good!

Come on, guys!
Me too.
Seriously?

MY LANGUAGE NOTES

Self-check

Vocabulary

1 Complete the sentences with one word in each gap.

0 In the morning, I *get* up at seven o'clock.

1 We ________ lessons all day.

2 After school, I ________ out with friends.

3 We ________ computer games on Saturdays.

4 After dinner, I ________ TV.

5 At night, I ________ to bed at nine o'clock.

2 Complete the sequences.

0	January	*February*	March
1	July		September
2	Friday		Sunday
3	October		December
4	March		May
5	Tuesday		Thursday

Grammar

3 Complete the sentences with the Present Simple form of the verb in brackets.

0 Tom *gets up* (get up) early.
1 We ________ (go) to a big school.
2 Sally ________ (like) chocolate ice cream.
3 Tim ________ (tidy) his room every day.
4 They ________ (live) in London.
5 I ________ (have) lunch in the park.

4 Rewrite the sentences with the adverb in the correct place.

0 They walk to school. (always)
They always walk to school.
1 I am busy in the afternoon. (usually)
____
2 We play tennis. (never)
____
3 Mum watches TV. (sometimes)
____
4 He is late for school. (always)
____
5 My cat sleeps on my bed. (often)
____

Speaking

5 Complete the dialogues with one word in each gap.

1 A: What [0] *time* is lunch?
B: It's at half [1] ________ twelve.
2 A: What time [2] ________ it?
B: It's ten [3] ________ to five.
3 A: What time is the film?
B: It's [4] ________ six o'[5] ________.

YOUR SCORE

Vocabulary	__/10	Speaking	__/5
Grammar	__/10	**Total:**	__/25

On the Portal
Extra Practice Activities: Self-check

Quick Progress Check Units 1–6

Reading and Writing

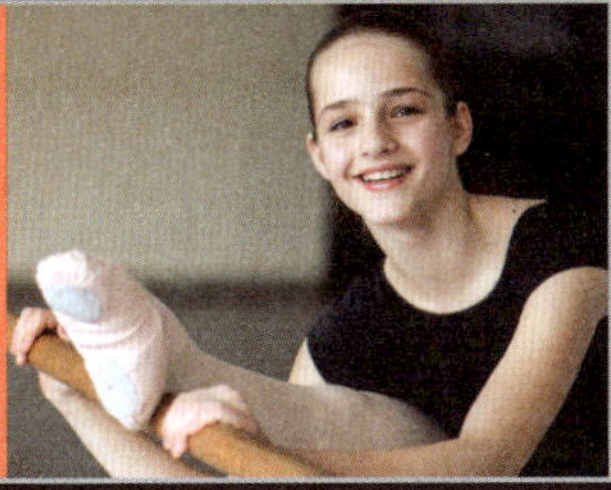

My name is Justine. I'm twelve and I'm a dancer. I'm sometimes on TV!

I always get up at half past six. I have breakfast and then I go to school. My school is a special dancing school. We have dancing lessons after school on Mondays, Wednesdays and Fridays. We often make videos. That's very cool. Then I go home and do my homework. I have dinner and speak to my family. I usually go to bed at half past nine.

At the weekend, I usually hang out with my best friend, Madalena. We are classmates. We talk about our lessons and watch videos about our favourite dancers.

1 Read the text. Complete the sentences with one word in each gap.

0 Justine can *dance*.
1 She goes to school after ________ .
2 She has dancing lessons ________ days a week.
3 She ________ her ________ before dinner.
4 Justine and Madalena like watching videos about their favourite ________ .

2 Write sentences about what Alice does on Mondays.

0 get up 07:15
1 have breakfast 08:00
2 go to school 08:30
3 do homework 16.45
4 have dinner 19.10

0 *Alice gets up at quarter past seven.*
1 ________
2 ________
3 ________
4 ________

Vocabulary and Grammar

3 Choose the correct option.

0 Birds can *swim* / *fly*, but fish *can* / *can't*.
1 I usually *draw* / *write* my name *on* / *next to* my notebooks.
2 She *doesn't* / *don't* go to bed early at *Saturday* / *the weekend*.
3 *Has he* / *He has* got *round* / *dark* hair?
4 We *always* / *never* watch TV after breakfast. We *hasn't* / *haven't* got time.
5 Jules *tidy* / *tidies* her room every morning *before* / *after* she gets up.

Listening

4 6.4 Julie is with her mum's friend, Mrs Williams. Mrs Williams has got some family photos. Listen and match names 1–4 with a–e.

0 Rob *b* a can cook cupcakes.
1 Ann ☐ b can play basketball.
2 Barney ☐ c goes swimming on Saturday.
3 Karen ☐ d is Barney's friend.
4 May ☐ e is twelve.

Speaking

5 Complete the dialogues with one word in each gap.

0 Alex: Can you sing?
Kim: *Yes*, I can!
1 Alex: Let's go to Music Club.
Kim: It's not a good ________ .
2 Alex: I know! We can go to the cinema!
Kim: ________ do that!
3 Alex: What time is the film?
Kim: It's ________ half past five.
4 Alex: Let's ask Michelle to come.
Kim: OK, we ________ phone her.

YOUR SCORE

Reading and Writing:	__/8	Listening:	__/4
Vocabulary and Grammar:	__/5	Speaking:	__/4
		Total:	__/21

Reading Time 3

Good boy, Eddie!

1

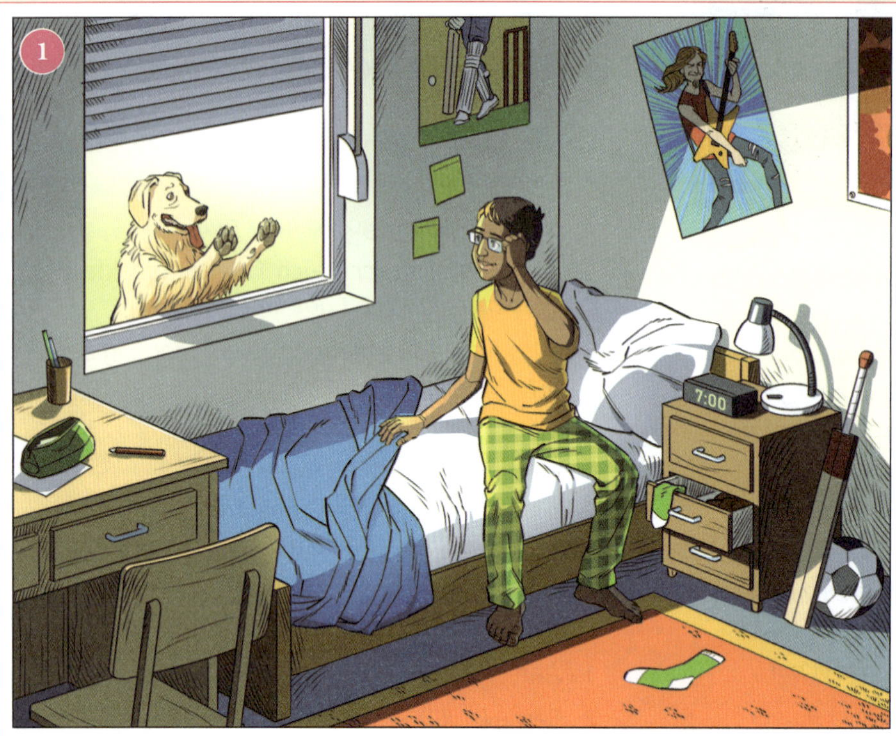

It's 7 a.m. Rishi is in bed, but Eddie, his dog, is ready for his morning walk in the park. Rishi can see the top of Eddie's head from his bedroom window. 'Woof! Woof!' Eddie barks at Rishi.

'OK, OK!' Rishi says. He gets up and goes to the bathroom.

'Woof!' Eddie is now outside the bathroom window.

'Hang on a minute!' Rishi shouts. He brushes his teeth. Then he puts on his tracksuit.

'Can I have an egg for breakfast first?' he asks. Eddie barks again.

'That's a no, then,' says Rishi. He takes a small bottle of orange juice from the fridge and an apple and goes out.

2

At the park, Rishi and Eddie play Eddie's favourite game. Rishi throws a ball, Eddie runs, catches it in his mouth and brings it back to Rishi. He does that four or five times. Rishi throws the ball again. This time, Eddie runs and runs. Rishi can't see him. 'Eddie! Eddie! Where are you?'

Eddie comes back. A woman is with him. Eddie has got something in his mouth, but it isn't the ball.

'What's that?' says Rishi.'Let me see.'

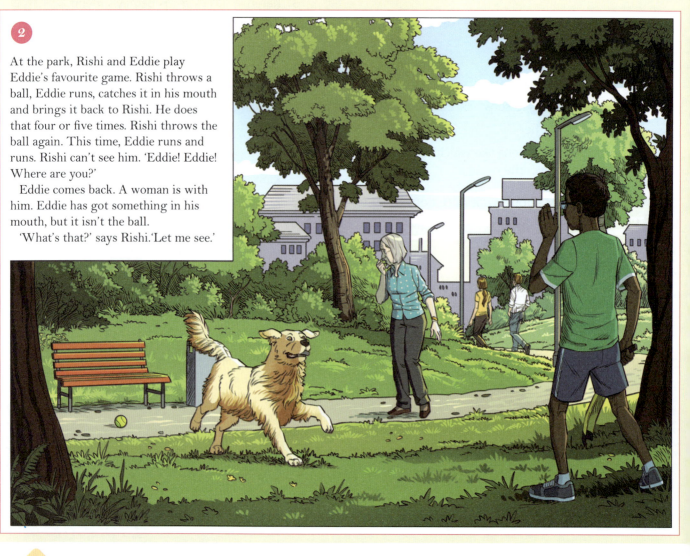

Before you read

1 Match pictures A–D with the words below.

A

B

C

D

2 Look at the pictures on page 70. What do you think happens in the story?

While you read

3 RT3.1 Read and listen to the story. Then choose the correct answer.

1 It's 7 a.m. Eddie wants
   a to go inside the house.
   b to eat.
   c to go to the park.

2 What about Rishi's breakfast?
   a He has an egg for breakfast at home.
   b He has orange juice and an apple at the park.
   c He has orange juice and an apple at home.

3 At the park, Eddie's favourite game is to
   a play with a ball.
   b run.
   c bark.

4 RT3.2 What has Eddie got in his mouth? Guess. Then listen and find out.

a key ring with a red shoe

a ring with a blue stone

After you read

5 Read the descriptions of the things in Exercise 4. Then describe pictures 1–4. Use *with*.

1

bag / white cat

____

2

T-shirt / red car

____

3

boy / blue eyes

____

4

girl / red hair

____

6 What do you think of the story? Colour the stars.

Animals 7

VOCABULARY
Wild animals | Pets | Adjectives | Where animals live

GRAMMAR
Present Simple negative | Present Simple questions and short answers

7.1 Vocabulary
Wild animals

1 Match animals A–H with words 1–8.

A 

B 

C 

D 

E 

F 

G 

H 

1 [D] crocodile 2 [ ] frog 3 [ ] butterfly 4 [ ] kangaroo
5 [ ] lion 6 [ ] monkey 7 [ ] snake 8 [ ] whale

2 Which animal is different? Choose the odd one out. Then match it with the correct reason a–e.

1 [c] fish crocodile frog (spider)
2 [ ] snake butterfly bird fly
3 [ ] elephant fish monkey tiger
4 [ ] lion tiger giraffe bird
5 [ ] tiger whale snake fish

a It lives in water.
b It can fly.
c It can't swim.
d It can't fly.
e It's got legs.

3 Choose the correct option.

1 *Frogs* / (*Crocodiles*) have got big mouths.
2 *Whales* / *Frogs* live in the sea.
3 *Spiders* / *Snakes* are very long.
4 *Tigers* / *Birds* can fly.
5 *Frogs* / *Snakes* can jump.
6 *Spiders* / *Lions* have got eight legs.
7 *Kangaroos* / *Monkeys* can climb trees.

4 What can animals do? Write two animals under each verb. Use words from Exercise 2.

swim	run	fly
crocodile	*elephant*	*bird*
______	______	______

 I can talk about wild animals.

On the Portal
Extra Practice Activities: Lesson 7.1

7.2 Grammar

Present Simple negative

1 Choose the correct option.

1 My parents *don't* / *doesn't* play computer games.
2 I *don't* / *doesn't* get up early on Saturday.
3 Lucy *don't* / *doesn't* like cats.
4 We *don't* / *doesn't* hang out on Monday.
5 Josh *don't* / *doesn't* go to school by bike.
6 We *don't* / *doesn't* have lessons on Sunday.
7 You *don't* / *doesn't* tidy your bedroom every morning.
8 Elephants *don't* / *doesn't* eat fish.

2 Complete the sentences with the Present Simple form of the verb in brackets.

1 My pet *doesn't like* (not like) chocolate.
2 I ______ (not tidy) my room every day.
3 We ______ (not watch) TV before dinner.
4 My little sister ______ (not go) to school.
5 You ______ (not like) pop music.
6 My cousin ______ (not speak) French.

3 Make affirmative (✓) and negative (✗) sentences in the Present Simple.

1 my cat / ✓ like / this red ball!
My cat likes this red ball.
2 cats / ✗ eat / cupcakes
Cats don't eat cupcakes.
3 my friend / ✓ play / in the garden
______
4 my sister / ✗ tidy / her bedroom
______
5 Joe and Amy / ✓ hang out / after school
______
6 we / ✗ go / to school / on Sunday
______

4 Look at the table. Correct the sentences.

	get up early	play computer games	listen to classical music
Jen	✗	✓	✗
Alex	✗	✓	✓
Mum	✓	✗	✓
Dad	✗	✗	✓

1 Jen, Alex and Dad get up early.
Jen, Alex and Dad don't get up early.
2 Dad gets up early.
______
3 Jen and Alex don't play computer games.
______
4 Mum and Dad play computer games.
______
5 Mum doesn't listen to classical music.
______
6 Jen listens to classical music.
______

5 Match sentences 1–7 with animals a–g.

1 [a] It's got small ears.
2 [ ] It can fly.
3 [ ] It lives in water.
4 [ ] It's got long ears.
5 [ ] It's got a long body.
6 [ ] It doesn't walk fast!
7 [ ] Its babies are puppies.

a a hamster
b a tortoise
c a parrot
d a rabbit
e a goldfish
f an iguana
g a dog

6 Complete the sentences so they are true for you.

1 On Wednesday, I ______ .
2 On Sunday, I don't ______ .
3 On Monday, my friend ______ .
4 On Saturday, my friend doesn't ______ .

I can use the negative form of the Present Simple and talk about pets.

On the Portal
Extra Practice Activities: Lesson 7.2

7.3 Grammar

Present Simple questions and short answers

1 Choose the correct option.

1 *Do* / *Does* you know Mari?
2 *Do* / *Does* Tom live in a house with a garden?
3 *Do* / *Does* your friends speak English?
4 *Do* / *Does* your mum make nice cakes?
5 *Do* / *Does* I sing well?
6 *Do* / *Does* you and your sister like cats?

2 Match answers a–f with questions 1–6 in Exercise 1.

a ☐ Yes, she does.
b ☐ No, you don't.
c ☐ *1* Yes, I do.
d ☐ Yes, we do.
e ☐ No, they don't.
f ☐ Yes, he does.

3 Complete the dialogue with *do*, *does*, *don't* or *doesn't*.

Reporter: [1]*Do* you speak any foreign languages, Superdug?
Superdug: No, I [2]________.
Reporter: [3]________ Kit speak any foreign languages?
Superdug: Yes, she [4]________.
Reporter: [5]________ you and Kit work together?
Superdug: Yes, we [6]________, but Kit [7]________ wear a superhero suit!

4 Write questions.

1 Suzie goes to school at eight o'clock.
Does Suzie go to school at eight o'clock?
2 Mike plays football at school.
____
3 Lucy has piano lessons on Monday.
____
4 Dave watches videos to relax.
____
5 Rosie tidies her bedroom on Saturday.
____

5 Make questions in the Present Simple.

1 you / speak Chinese?
Do you speak Chinese?
2 you / like chocolate?
____
3 your teacher / ride a bike to school?
____
4 your friends / play football on Saturday?
____
5 you / hang out with your friends at the weekend?
____
6 your dad / go to the gym?
____

6 Write short answers to the questions in Exercise 5 so they are true for you.

1 *No, I don't.*
2 ________________
3 ________________
4 ________________
5 ________________
6 ________________

7 Complete the questions with *do* or *does* and the verbs below.

~~do~~ drink go have play speak take

1 A: What *do* you *do* after school?
B: I usually hang out with my friends.
2 A: What ________ Sandra ________ for dinner on Fridays?
B: Pizza!
3 A: When ________ they ________ tennis?
B: At the weekend.
4 A: What ________ your pet ________?
B: Water, of course.
5 A: What time ________ you ________ to bed?
B: At ten o'clock.
6 A: ________ your best friend ________ any foreign languages?
B: Yes! My best friend is French!
7 A: When ________ you ________ your dog for a walk?
B: In the afternoon, after school.

 I can ask and answer questions in the Present Simple.

On the Portal
Extra Practice Activities: Lesson 7.3

7.4 Speaking

Buying a ticket

1 7.1 Listen and repeat the phrases.

SPEAKING Buying a ticket

A: Can I help you?
B: Can I have *one ticket*/*two tickets to the zoo*, please?
A: That's *eighteen pounds fifty*.
B: Here you are.
A: Here's your ticket./Here are your tickets.
B: Thanks.

2 Read the dialogue and choose the correct option.

A: Can I help you?
B: [1]*Can I have* / *Would you like* a ticket to the museum, please?
A: [2]*Would* / *Do* you like a guide?
B: No, [3]*thanks* / *please*.
A: That's £8.50, please.
B: Here [4]*are you* / *you are*.
A: [5]*They're* / *Here are* your tickets.
B: Thank you.

3 Complete the dialogue with the phrases below.

and here's | can I have | ~~can I help~~ | here you are | that's | would you like

Assistant: [1]*Can I help* you?
Customer: Yes, please. [2]________ a sandwich, please?
Assistant: Yes, OK. [3]________ a drink too?
Customer: Yes, please. I'd like some water.
Assistant: [4]________ £4.25, please.
Customer: [5]________.
Assistant: Thank you. [6]________ your sandwich.

4 Complete the table.

1		£5.50	*five pounds fifty*
2		£____	two pounds fifty
3		£8.90	________
4		£____	four pounds thirty
5		£1.20	________

5 Complete the dialogue with one word in each gap.

A: Hello. [1]*Can* I help you?
B: Hi. Can I [2]________ two tickets, [3]________?
A: Sure. Would you [4]________ a bag of popcorn?
B: [5]________, please. Good idea!
A: [6]________ £15, please.
B: [7]________ you are.
A: Here [8]________ your tickets and [9]________'s the popcorn. Enjoy the film!
B: Thanks.

I can buy a ticket.

On the Portal
Extra Practice Activities: Lesson 7.4

7.5 Reading and Vocabulary

Sharks

ALL ABOUT ... SHARKS

Are all sharks dangerous to people?
No, not all sharks are dangerous to us, but we are very dangerous to sharks! Why? Sharks don't often eat people, but in some countries people eat sharks.

What do sharks usually eat?
They eat fish and other sea animals. They sometimes eat other sharks.

What can they do?
Sharks are strong and they can swim fast. They can see and smell under water very well.

Can they hear?
Good question. It's amazing. They haven't got ears like our ears, but they can hear fish from hundreds of kilometres away!

1 Look at the photos. Mark the adjectives T (true) or F (false).

1 fast  T / F

2 strong  T / F

3 dangerous T / F

4 cute T / F

5 ugly T / F

6 slow  T / F

2 Tick (✓) the words that describe sharks and put a cross (✗) for the words that don't describe them.

dangerous ✓ slow ☐ strong ☐ lots of teeth ☐
long body ☐ cute face ☐ big ears ☐

3 Read the text. Choose the correct option.

1 Sharks are *sometimes* / *always* dangerous to people.
2 People *are* / *aren't* a problem for sharks.
3 Sharks don't usually eat *sea animals* / *other sharks*.
4 They *have got* / *haven't got* very good eyes.
5 They *can* / *can't* hear very well.

4 Read the text again. Answer the questions.

1 What do sharks usually eat?
______
2 Do they often eat people?
______
3 Can they smell well?
______
4 What can they hear?
______

 I can understand a text about sharks.

On the Portal
Extra Practice Activities: Lesson 7.5

7.6 Listening and Writing

Pets

1 7.2 Listen to Emma and Ted. Tick (✓) the pets Emma has got.

A ☐

B ☐

C ☐

2 7.2 Listen again. Answer the questions.

1 Where are the pets?
They're in Emma's bedroom.
2 Are they brothers or sisters?
....
3 What colour is Ted's favourite pet?
....
4 What do Emma's pets need every day?
....
5 Where does their special food come from?
....

3 7.2 Listen again. Choose the correct option.

1 There are *two / three* pets.
2 Emma says they *are / aren't* easy to look after.
3 They *like / don't like* fruit.
4 Ted has got some *hamsters / rabbits*.

4 Read the email. Choose the correct option.

Hi Sam,

I know you like cats. Well, our cat has got some kittens. Would you like one? They're cute. Three are black, two are black and white, and one is grey. They haven't got names. They're very young. They're very friendly too!

Kittens eat special kitten food, but they don't eat a lot. They drink water, but milk isn't good for them.

Kittens are easy to look after. They don't go for walks and they sleep a lot.

Can you ask your mum and dad? Let me know.

Ben

1 Does Sam like cats?
Yes, he does. / No, he doesn't.
2 How many kittens are there?
There are three. / There are six.
3 Have they got names?
Yes, they have. / No, they haven't.
4 Do they eat a lot?
Yes, they do. / No, they don't.
5 Can Sam have a kitten?
Yes, he can. / We don't know.

WRITING TIME

5 You have got some puppies. Write an email to a friend and offer him/her one of them.

1 Find ideas
Use the words below or your own ideas.

black and brown
cute, funny, friendly
✓ special puppy food
✓ water ✗ milk
sleep and play

2 Draft
Begin the email.
Hi/Hello (+ your friend's name).
Explain why you are writing.
Describe the puppies.
They are ... They eat/drink/like/play ...
End your email.
Can you ask your mum and dad? Let me know.
Write your name.

3 Check and write
Check the beginning and ending of your email. Write the final version of your text.

I can understand and write short texts about pets.

On the Portal
Extra Practice Activities: Lesson 7.6

7.7 CLIL: Science

The environment

1 Find seven environment words. Then look at the photos and complete the sentences.

A	O	S	E	A	D	L
T	R	E	E	S	A	A
R	H	G	Y	F	M	N
F	O	R	P	O	N	D
K	L	O	B	R	E	P
V	E	U	O	E	A	W
C	E	N	T	S	U	A
N	Q	D	I	T	G	B

1 Some animals live in the *sea*.

2 Some animals live on ________.

3 Some animals live in a ________.

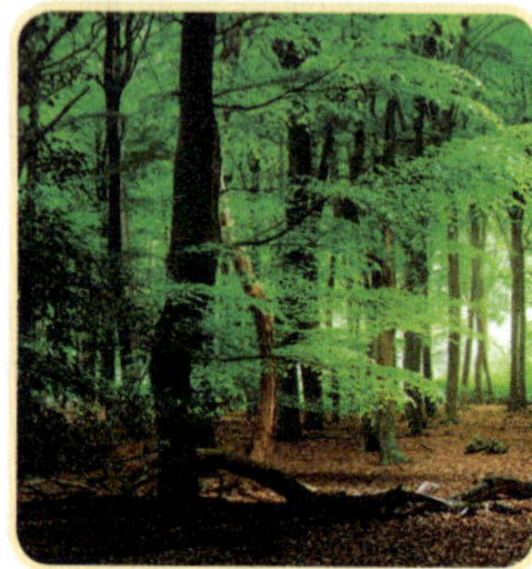

4 Some animals live in the ________.

5 Some animals live in a ________ in the ________.

6 Some animals live in ________.

2 Where do these animals live? Write S (sea) or L (land).

1 [*L*] 2 [ ]

3 [ ] 4 [ ]

5 [ ] 6 [ ]

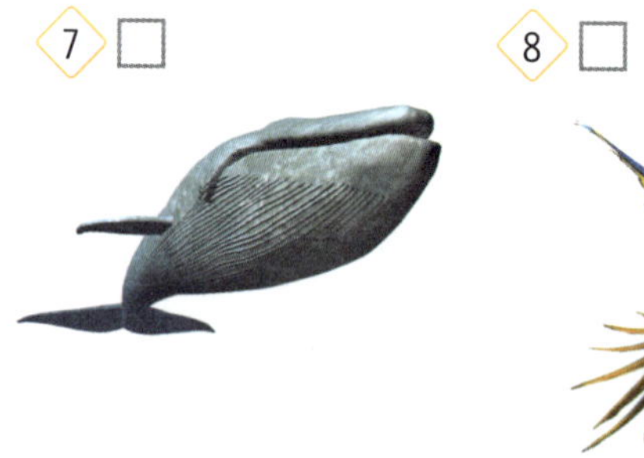

7 [ ] 8 [ ]

3 Complete the sentences.

1 Whales and fish live in the *s e a*.
2 Frogs and small fish live in a _ _ _ _.
3 Rabbits and groundhogs live in a hole in the _ _ _ _ _ _.
4 Elephants and tigers live in the _ _ _ _ _ _.
5 Monkeys and birds live in _ _ _ _ _.

 I can say and write about where animals live.

My Language File

WORDLIST 7.3

Wild animals

bird (n)
butterfly (n)
crocodile (n)
elephant (n)
fish (n)
fly (n)
frog (n)
giraffe (n)
kangaroo (n)
lion (n)
monkey (n)
snake (n)
spider (n)
tiger (n)
whale (n)

Pets

cat (n)
dog (n)
goldfish (n)
hamster (n)
iguana (n)
parrot (n)
rabbit (n)
tortoise (n)

Adjectives

cute (adj)
dangerous (adj)
fast (adj)
slow (adj)
strong (adj)
ugly (adj)

Where animals live

in a hole in the ground
in a pond
in the forest
in the sea
in trees
on land

Extra words

amazing (adj)
at 55 kilometres an hour
at the weekend
because (conjunction)
children (singular: child) (n)
dog food (n)
drink (v)
easy (adj)
every day
expert (n)
food (n)
foreign language
guide (n)
hard work
have fun
hour (n)
I could eat a horse!
I'm allergic to …
interview (n)
kilo (n)
leaves (singular: leaf) (n)
litre (n)
look after (v)
magazine (n)
night (n)
not … at all
pass (n)
puppy (n)
relax (v)
reporter (n)
sleep (v)
take the dog for a walk
think (v)
together (adv)
water (n)
win (v)
work (v)

Sounds good!

I don't mind!
Oh, all right!
Poor (dog)!

MY LANGUAGE NOTES

Self-check

Vocabulary

1 Match the letters to make pet words.

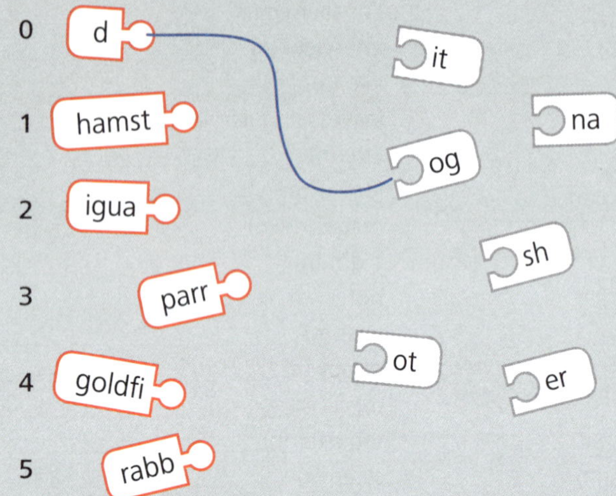

2 Look at the pictures and complete the words.

0 a c_u_ _t_ _e_ c _a_ t

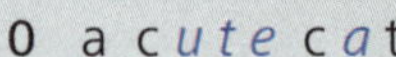

1 a f_ _ t b_ _ d

2 a d_ _ge_ _us l_ _n

3 a s_ _w t_ _to_ _e

4 an u_ _y f_ _

5 a st_ _ _g e_ _ph_ _t

Grammar

3 Complete the sentences with the Present Simple form of the verb in brackets.

0 I _don't get up_ (not get up) early at weekends.
1 My friend ________ (not sing) in a band.
2 We ________ (not live) in a big house.
3 Ella ________ (not like) vegetables.
4 I ________ (not speak) French very well.

4 Make questions in the Present Simple. Then answer yes (✓) or no (✗). Use short answers.

0 I / speak good English?
A: [0]_Do I speak good English?_
B: ✓ [00]_Yes, you do._
1 Tom / wear jeans to school?
A: [1]________
B: ✗ [2]________
2 your friends / like football?
A: [3]________
B: ✓ [4]________
3 your granny / visit you every week?
A: [5]________
B: ✓ [6]________

Speaking

5 Complete the dialogue with one word in each gap.

A: Hello, [0]_can_ I help [1]________ ?
B: Can I [2]________ two tickets, [3]________ ?
A: Yes, [4]________ fifteen pounds fifty.
B: Here you are.
A: Here [5]________ your tickets.

YOUR SCORE

Vocabulary:	__/10	Speaking:	__/5
Grammar:	__/10	**Total:**	__/25

On the Portal
Extra Practice Activities: Self-check

BBC CULTURE

Pets in the UK

1 Look at the photos and do the crossword.

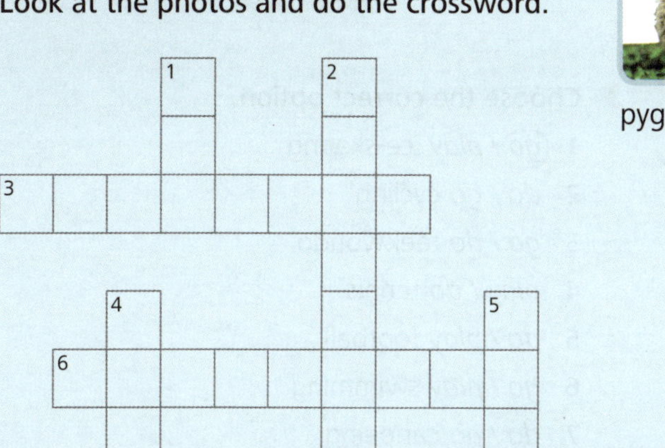

Across

3 pygmy h________

6 t________

7 f________

Down

1 d________

2 ax________

4 c________

5 r________

2 Complete the sentences with the words below.

cute ears eat legs live ~~popular~~ quiet run small unusual

1 Dogs are very *popular* pets. Some are big and some are ________ . They're very good friends!

2 Tarantulas are great pets. They're very ________ and they don't ________ a lot!

3 Rabbits are cute. They've got long ________ and they can jump and ________ fast.

4 Axolotls have an ________ name! They aren't fish, but they ________ in the water.

5 Pygmy hedgehogs are small and very ________ ! They've got short ________ , black eyes and a brown nose.

I like that!

8

VOCABULARY
Sports | Healthy lifestyle | Sports equipment

GRAMMAR
love / like / don't like / hate + -ing | Object pronouns | Question words

8.1 Vocabulary

Sports

1 Look at the photos. Choose the correct option.

1 (cycling) / taekwondo

2 hockey / badminton

3 canoeing / windsurfing

4 basketball / volleyball

5 tennis / table tennis

6 ice-skating / roller skating

2 Look at the pictures. Label the sports with words from Exercise 1.

1 *badminton*
2 ______
3 ______
4 ______
5 ______
6 ______

3 Choose the correct option.

1 *(go) / play* ice-skating
2 *do / go* cycling
3 *go / do* taekwondo
4 *play / go* tennis
5 *do / play* football
6 *go / play* swimming
7 *do / go* canoeing
8 *play / go* volleyball
9 *go / do* snowboarding
10 *play / do* badminton

4 Match the sentence halves.

1 [*d*] I sometimes play
2 [ ] George does
3 [ ] Do you go
4 [ ] My brother plays
5 [ ] Sandra never goes
6 [ ] Do you often play

a hockey with his friends.
b ice-skating.
c snowboarding with your friends?
d badminton with my dad.
e basketball at school?
f taekwondo every Monday.

 I can talk about sports.

On the Portal
Extra Practice Activities: Lesson 8.1

8.2 Grammar

love / like / don't like / hate + -ing | Object pronouns

1 Complete the sentences with the correct form of the verb in brackets. Who is it? Write *Jen, Alex, Lucas* or *Lian*.

1. This person loves *playing* (play) the guitar.
   Who? *Lucas*
2. This person likes ____________ (make) cupcakes.
   Who? ____________
3. This person hates ____________ (get up) early and ____________ (cook).
   Who? ____________
4. This person likes ____________ (skateboard) and ____________ (climb).
   Who? ____________

2 Complete the sentences with the words below.

doesn't like don't like ~~hate~~ hates like likes love loves

1. We ☹☹ *hate* rock climbing.
2. My parents ☺ ____________ windsurfing.
3. Ann ☹ ____________ playing football.
4. My grandad ☺☺ ____________ cooking.
5. My friends ☹ ____________ getting up early.
6. I ☺☺ ____________ cycling.
7. Mark ☺ ____________ playing basketball.
8. Mum ☹☹ ____________ swimming in cold water!

3 Look at the pictures. Complete the sentences with the correct form of *love, like, don't like* or *hate* and the words below.

climb eat ~~get~~ sleep

1 ☹☹ My cat *hates getting* wet.

2 ☺ She ____________ fish for lunch.

3 ☺☺ She ____________ trees in the garden.

4 ☹ She ____________ in her bed. She likes *my* bed!

4 Complete the sentences with object pronouns.

1. Emma is nice. I like *her* .
2. Ice-skating is fun. I love ____________ .
3. You are great at football. I like watching ____________ .
4. Amy and Tom are my best friends. I like ____________ .
5. Tom is my baby brother. I love ____________ .
6. We're good at dancing. Watch ____________ !

5 Complete the dialogue with the words below.

~~doing~~ hate her me playing plays she

A: What does your sister like [1]*doing* at the weekend?
B: Monica loves sports. [2]____________ often goes swimming or she [3]____________ tennis.
A: Do you play tennis with [4]____________ ?
B: No. I [5]____________ it. I love [6]____________ football! Do you want to play with [7]____________ and my friends?

I can use the verbs *love / like / don't like / hate + -ing* and object pronouns.

On the Portal
Extra Practice Activities: Lesson 8.2

Grammar

Question words

1 Read the dialogues and choose the correct option.

1 A: When is the football game?
B: *It's great. / It's on Saturday.*
2 A: Where's my mobile phone?
B: *It's on the table. / It's from China.*
3 A: Whose bike is next to the house?
B: *The bike is green. / It's my mum's bike.*
4 A: How many friends have you got?
B: *Five. / Five years old.*
5 A: What's in your bag?
B: *It's next to the desk. / There's a notebook.*
6 A: Who's your English teacher?
B: *Mr Evans is here. / It's Mr Evans.*

2 Read the dialogues and choose the correct option.

1 A: *Where / When* is Dug?
B: He's in a shopping centre.
2 A: *Who / Whose* is the woman?
B: She's Irina Peters.
3 A: *Who / What* is her sport?
B: It's tennis.
4 A: *What / Who* does Dug want?
B: He wants her autograph.
5 A: *How many / When* mobile phones can you see?
B: Two.

3 Match 1–6 with a–f to make questions.

1 Who [d] a do you live?
2 What [ ] b is in your bag?
3 Where [ ] c sisters have you got?
4 How many [ ] d is your best friend?
5 When [ ] e skateboard is that?
6 Whose [ ] f is your birthday?

4 Complete the dialogue with the words below.

how many ~~what~~ when where who whose

A: [1]*What*'s your name?
B: Baris.
A: [2]________ are you from?
B: I'm from Turkey, but I live in London now.
A: [3]________ friends have you got in London?
B: A lot! Six or seven.
A: [4]________ is your best friend?
B: Jacob. He's my classmate. We want to go to a party today.
A: [5]________ party is it?
B: It's my cousin's party. It's her birthday.
A: [6]________ is the party?
B: It's at five o'clock.

5 Make questions.

1 how many classmates / you / have got?
How many classmates have you got?
2 when / you / go to bed on Mondays?
____
3 where / your friends / hang out?
____
4 what / be / your favourite sport?
____
5 who / be / your favourite singer?
____

6 Answer the questions in Exercise 5 so they are true for you.

1 I've got ________ classmates.
2 ________
3 ________
4 ________
5 ________

 I can ask detailed questions.

On the Portal
Extra Practice Activities: Lesson 8.3

8.4 Speaking

Talking about the weather

1 🔊 8.1 Listen and repeat the phrases.

SPEAKING Talking about the weather

A: What's the weather like?
B: It's *cloudy/cold/hot/rainy/snowy/sunny/warm/windy.*
It's *cold/hot/rainy/sunny* in *winter/summer/autumn/spring.*

2 Order the sentences to make a dialogue.

a ☐ Oh, dear. That's horrible.
b ☐ It's cold and snowy here, but I like it.
c ☐ Well, I hate cold weather!
d *1* Hi, Mandy. Is the weather nice in Scotland?
e ☐ No, it isn't. It's rainy and cold!
f ☐ Yes, it's really horrible. What's the weather like in France?

3 Label the pictures.

1 *sunny*

2 ____________

3 ____________

4 ____________

5 ____________

6 ____________

7 ____________

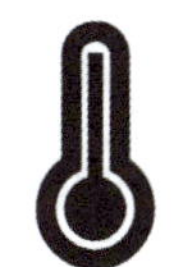

8 ____________

4 Complete the sentences with weather words.

1 It's *h o t*. Let's go swimming.
2 It's very c _ _ _ . Wear a coat.
3 It's w _ _ _ _ . Let's go windsurfing.
4 It's r _ _ _ _ . Let's stay at home.
5 It's s _ _ _ _ . Let's go snowboarding.
6 It's w _ _ _ . Wear a T-shirt.

5 Label the photos with the words below.

autumn spring summer winter

1 ____________

2 ____________

3 ____________

4 ____________

6 Choose the correct option.

1 It's sometimes hot in *(summer)* / *winter.*
2 It's *often / never* warm in spring.
3 It's always cold in *winter / spring.*
4 It's often rainy and *cloudy / sunny* in autumn.
5 It's never snowy in *winter / summer.*

7 Complete the dialogue with the words below.

hope hot like rainy wet ~~what~~

A: Hi, [1]*what*'s the weather [2]____________ in New York today?
B: It's windy and [3]____________ . I've got an umbrella!
A: I hate getting [4]____________ !
B: Me too! I [5]____________ it's sunny and [6]____________ tomorrow.

I can talk about the weather.

On the Portal
Extra Practice Activities: Lesson 8.4

8.5 Reading and Vocabulary

Healthy lifestyle

Sam is thirteen. He likes getting up early, but he goes to bed very late. He loves sports. He goes swimming before school. After school, he plays football. At the weekend, he goes cycling with his friends. Sam's sister Tammy is eleven. She doesn't like sport and she never does exercise. She likes reading and cooking. She goes to bed at ten and she gets up at half past six.

Sam loves cakes and he often eats pizza and chips, but Tammy doesn't usually eat them. Sam doesn't like fruit and he hates vegetables, but Tammy loves them. Tammy likes chocolate, but she doesn't eat it a lot. Sam usually drinks cola, but Tammy doesn't like it. She drinks fruit juice or water.

Who is healthy, Tammy or Sam?

1 Read the text. Choose the correct option.

	Sam	Tammy
do exercise	**1** often / sometimes	**2** usually / never
eat healthy food	**3** yes / no	**4** yes / no

2 Read the text again. Answer the questions.

1 What exercise does Sam do in the morning?
He goes swimming.

2 What does he do at the weekend?
______

3 What does Tammy like doing?
______

4 What does Sam like eating?
______

5 Does Tammy like fruit and vegetables?
______

6 What does Sam usually drink?
______

3 Match 1–6 with a–f.

1 [d] eat
2 [ ] drink
3 [ ] do
4 [ ] brush
5 [ ] have
6 [ ] go

a your teeth
b exercise
c friends
d fruit and vegetables
e to bed early
f a lot of water

4 Complete the text with words from Exercise 3.

I always [1] *brush* my [2] ______ in the morning and after dinner. I eat a lot of [3] ______ and [4] ______ . I love apples and oranges. I [5] ______ some [6] ______ every week. I often go cycling or swimming. I usually [7] ______ to [8] ______ early, at eight.

 I can understand short texts about healthy habits.

On the Portal
Extra Practice Activities: Lesson 8.5

8.6 Listening and Writing

Lifestyles

1 Match topics 1–3 with photos A–C.

1 food ☐ 2 sleep ☐ 3 exercise ☐

A

B

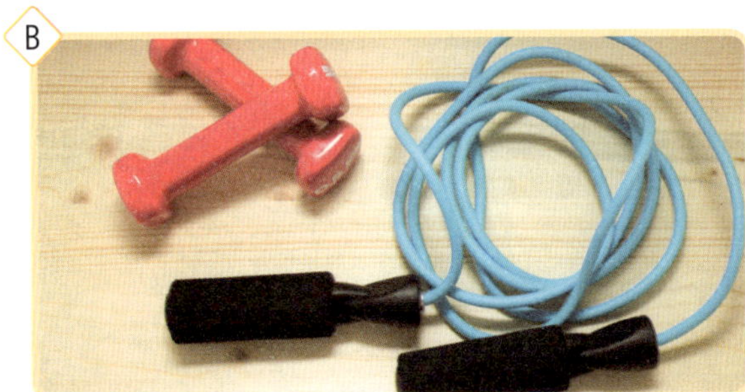

C

2 🔊 8.2 Listen to the dialogue. Match the questions to the topics in Exercise 1.

Question 1: ____________

Question 2: ____________

Question 3: ____________

3 🔊 8.2 Listen again. Complete the sentences about Tom.

Question 1

Tom's favourite food is [1]*chips* .

He eats a lot of [2]__________ and vegetables.

He drinks a lot of [3]__________ .

Question 2

He likes [4]__________ .

He always [5]__________ to school.

He sometimes goes [6]__________ .

Question 3

He goes to bed at [7]__________ .

He goes to sleep at [8]__________ .

4 Read the text. Correct the underlined mistakes 1–8.

> *likes*
> Andy [1]~~like~~ pizza, but he [2]<u>don't</u> eat it very often. He [3]<u>has always</u> lunch at school. He often eats a sandwich. He likes [4]<u>read</u>, but he doesn't [5]<u>likes</u> sport very much. His favourite sport [6]<u>are</u> swimming. He has swimming lessons on Fridays. Andy goes to bed [7]<u>in</u> nine because he likes [8]<u>sleep</u>. He doesn't get up early.

WRITING TIME

5 Write about May's lifestyle.

1 Find ideas

Use the information in the table.

food and drink?	fruit ☹ vegetables ☺☺ a lot of water
exercise? 	do taekwondo ☺ play badminton / at the weekend walk to school / always
go to bed? **get up?** 	10:00 p.m. / usually 7.30 a.m.

2 Draft

Write about May's lifestyle.

3 Check and write

Check for grammar mistakes and write the final version of your text.

I can understand and write short texts about healthy lifestyles.

On the Portal
Extra Practice Activities: Lesson 8.6

CLIL: Sports

Sports equipment

1 Look at the pictures and complete the dialogue.

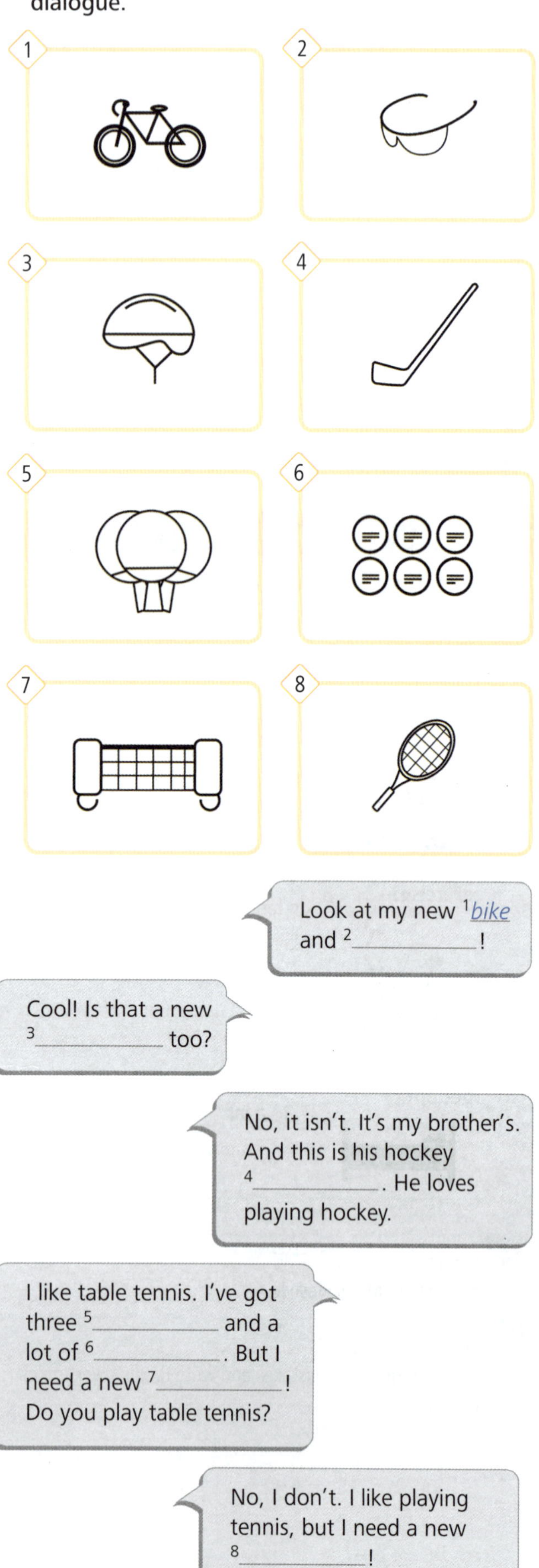

1
2
3
4
5
6
7
8
Look at my new ¹bike and ²________!
Cool! Is that a new ³________ too?
No, it isn't. It's my brother's. And this is his hockey ⁴________. He loves playing hockey.
I like table tennis. I've got three ⁵________ and a lot of ⁶________. But I need a new ⁷________!
Do you play table tennis?
No, I don't. I like playing tennis, but I need a new ⁸________!

2 Write the words below in the correct group.

cycling hockey ~~snowboarding~~ swimming tennis volleyball

1

2

3

4

5
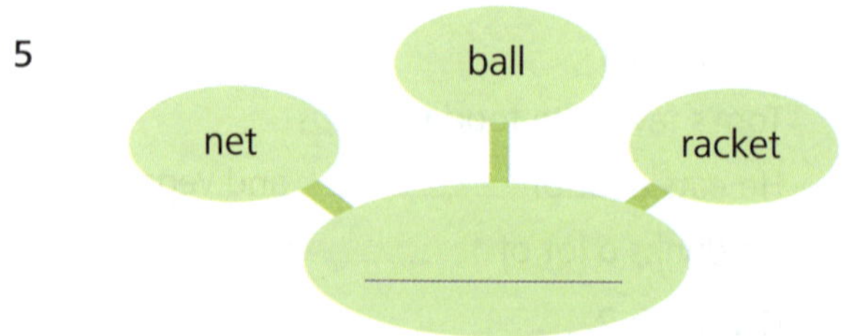

6

 I can name sports equipment.

My Language File

WORDLIST 8.3

Sports

badminton (n) ______
basketball (n) ______
canoeing (n) ______
cycling (n) ______
football (n) ______
hockey (n) ______
ice-skating (n) ______
roller skating (n) ______
skateboarding (n) ______
snowboarding (n) ______
swimming (n) ______
table tennis (n) ______
taekwondo (n) ______
tennis (n) ______
volleyball (n) ______
windsurfing (n) ______

Healthy lifestyle

brush your teeth ______
do exercise ______
drink a lot of water ______
eat fruit and vegetables ______
go to bed early ______
have friends ______

Sports equipment

bat (n) ______
goggles (n) ______
helmet (n) ______
net (n) ______
racket (n) ______
stick (n) ______

Extra words

appointment (n) ______
at the beach ______
autograph (n) ______
autumn (n) ______
champion (n) ______
chocolate (n) ______
cloudy (adj) ______
cold (adj) ______
competition (n) ______
fan (n) ______
find (v) ______
for example ______
from … to … ______
get wet ______
hate (v) ______
health (n) ______
healthy (adj) ______
horse-riding (n) ______
hot (adj) ______
I hope … ______
in the morning ______
meal (n) ______
pizza (n) ______
rainy (adj) ______
right now ______
rock climbing (n) ______
snowy (adj) ______
sporty (adj) ______
spring (n) ______
summer (n) ______
summer camp (n) ______
sunny (adj) ______
That's a pity. ______
tip (n) ______
want (v) ______
warm (adj) ______
water sport (n) ______
Well done! ______
What's the weather like? ______
whose (pronoun) ______
windy (adj) ______
winter (n) ______

Sounds good!

Maybe. ______
That's true. ______

MY LANGUAGE NOTES

Self-check

Vocabulary

1 Find the odd one out.

0 (roller skating) tennis football hockey
1 table tennis taekwondo badminton tennis
2 canoeing windsurfing swimming ice-skating
3 spring January winter summer
4 hot warm autumn sunny
5 snowy cold windy early

2 Look at the photos and complete the words.

0 do e*xercise*

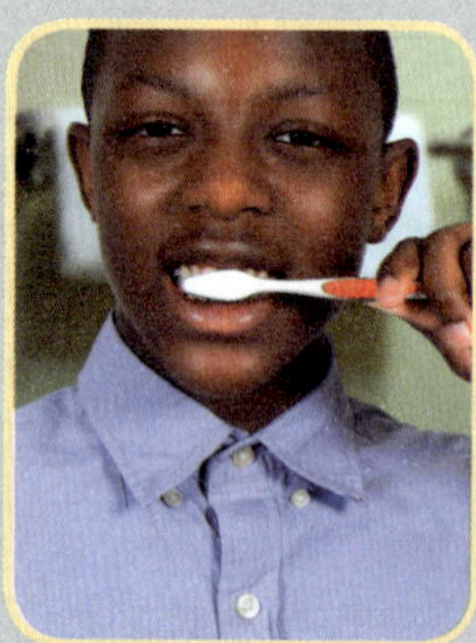
1 b________ my teeth

2 p________ badminton

3 g________ roller skating

4 d________ a lot of water

5 eat f________ and vegetables

Grammar

3 Make sentences.

0 Jack / hate / play / tennis
Jack hates playing tennis.
1 my sister / not like / roller skate
____
2 you / like / swim?
____
3 I / love / sing
____
4 we / not like / get up / early
____
5 your friends / like / eat / pizza?
____

4 Complete the sentences with one word in each gap.

0 A: *Who* is she?
B: She's my aunt.
1 A: ________ are you?
B: I'm at school.
2 A: ________ many cakes are there?
B: Six.
3 Your parents are nice. I like ________ .
4 Where's Emma? I can't see ________ .
5 Look at that picture! Do you like ________ ?

Speaking

5 Complete the dialogue with one word in each gap.

A: [0]*What*'s the weather [1]________ ?
B: [2]________ cold and rainy.
A: Is [3]________ windy too?
B: Yes, it [4]________ . I hope it's sunny tomorrow.
A: [5]________ too!

YOUR SCORE

Vocabulary:	__/10	Speaking:	__/5
Grammar:	__/10	**Total:**	**__/25**

On the Portal
Extra Practice Activities: Self-check

Quick Progress Check Units 1–8

Happy families

Jimbo, Sasha and Cheeky are our three new babies at City Zoo!

Jimbo's ears are big and he's got a very long nose! He loves playing in the water. People at the zoo love him. He's friendly and very cute.

Cheeky is with his mum and dad. He's very cute. His face is pink, but his parents' faces are black! He's a baby, so he doesn't eat food. He drinks milk. His mum and dad can climb trees, but Cheeky can't. He's too small.

Sasha is a white baby bird. Her mum likes eating insects, but Sasha can't eat them. She's too small. She can't fly and she can't run, but her parents can fly and run … on water!

Reading and Writing

1 Read the text. Match animals 1–3 with photos A–C.

1 Jimbo ☐
2 Sasha ☐
3 Cheeky ☐

2 Read the text again. Answer the questions.

0 Where are Jimbo, Sasha and Cheeky?
They're at City Zoo.
1 Where does Jimbo play?
2 Is Jimbo a dangerous animal?
3 What colour is Cheeky's dad's face?
4 What does Cheeky drink?
5 Who likes eating insects?
6 Can Sasha fly?

Vocabulary and Grammar

3 Look at the photo. Choose the correct option.

Jimmy's got a pet [0]*parrot / tortoise*. Her name is Suzie. She [1]*drinks / eats* parrot food and bananas. Suzie [2]*can / does* speak! She's very [3]*ugly / clever* and cute. She [4]*can / likes* playing with a ball and she loves [5]*looking / watching* TV!

Listening

4 8.4 Listen and complete the notes.

Sports in my town

0 Name of sports centre: *Hillside*
1 Where: ________ the cinema
2 Number of sports: ________
3 Team sports: football, ________ and basketball
4 Type of food in café: ________ food

Speaking

5 Complete dialogue with the words below. There is one extra word.

have help here is ~~let's~~ that's

A: [0]*Let's* go to the zoo!
B: Good idea!
C: Can I [1]________ you?
A: Can I [2]________ two tickets to the zoo, please?
C: [3]________ five pounds forty.
A: [4]________ you are.
C: And here are your tickets.
A: Thanks.

YOUR SCORE

Reading and Writing:	__/9	Listening:	__/4
Vocabulary and Grammar:	__/5	Speaking:	__/4
		Total:	__/22

The camping holiday

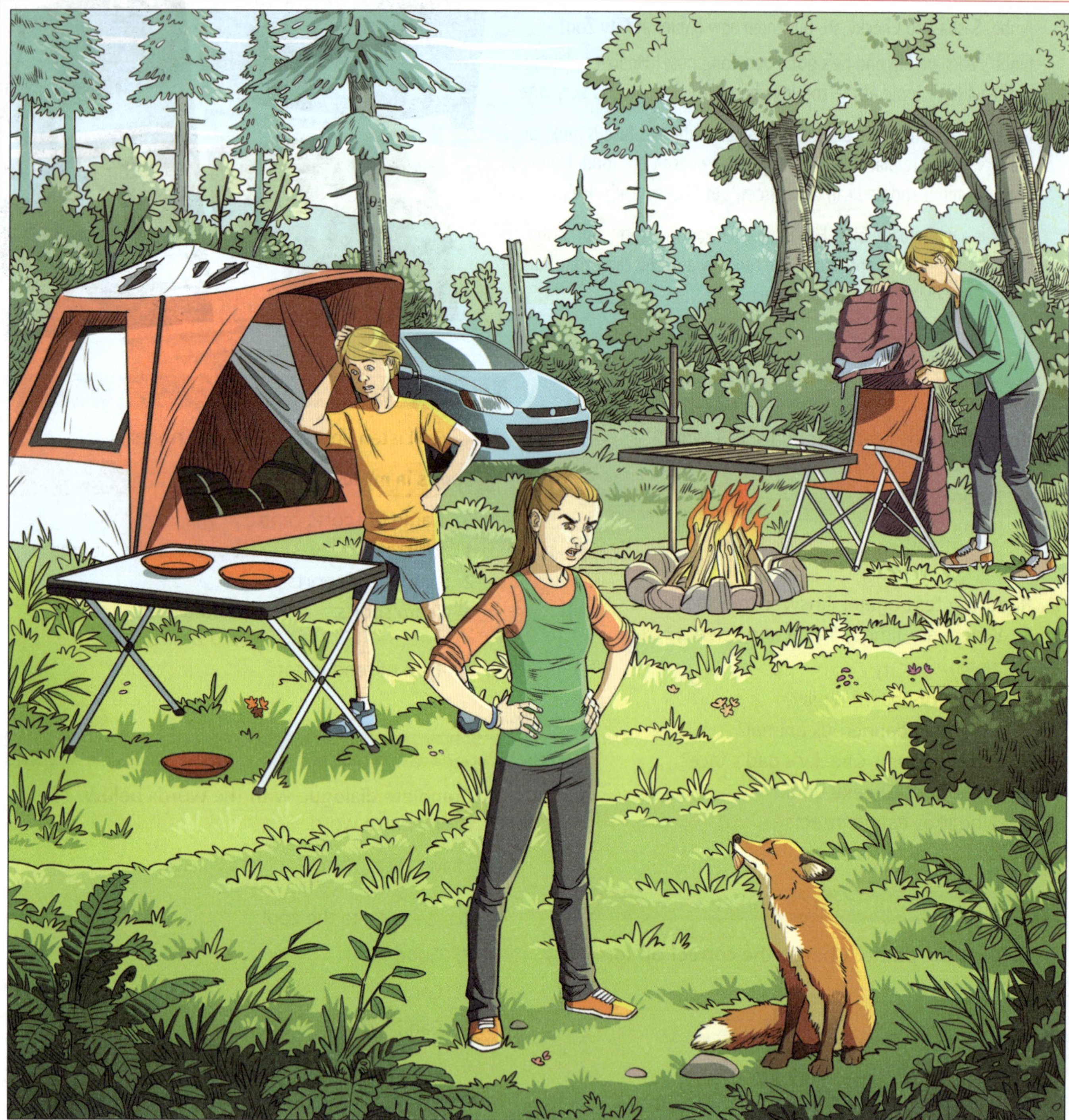

Let me tell you about our family camping holiday. It's summer, but this is the UK: it's warm and sunny in the morning, it rains in the afternoon and it's cloudy and cold in the evening. We've got a big tent for the three of us. It's old and there are holes in it, but we don't know it.

At dinner time, we make a fire and cook some food. We're all very hungry. I'm cold and I go to the tent to get my jacket. My jacket is wet. Our sleeping bags are wet too!

We put our plates on the camping table and take our things out of the tent. We put the sleeping bags next to the fire to dry.

'Er … Katia, where's our food?' my brother Greg asks.

I look at my plate. There's a fox next to it, but there isn't any food on it. The fox looks at me and then it runs away with my dinner!

'It's OK,' says Mum. 'We've got cake in the green bag. It's in the car.'

I go to the car. 'Is it the green bag with the yellow circles?' I ask.

'Yes, that's right!'

'There's a bottle of water in it, but there isn't any cake!'

My brother's face is very red. 'Oh, no! It's at home! I'm sorry. It's my fault!' he says.

Then it starts to rain again …

Before you read

1 Match sentences 1–4 with photos A–D.

1 This is a tent. ☐
2 There are holes in this jumper. ☐
3 This is how we make a fire. ☐
4 She's warm in her sleeping bag. ☐

A

B

C
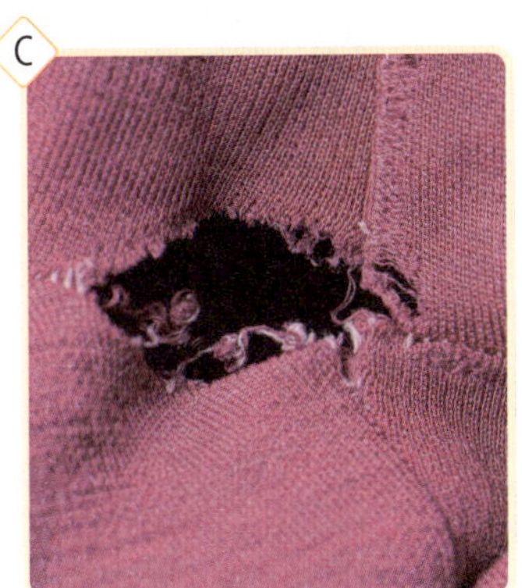

D
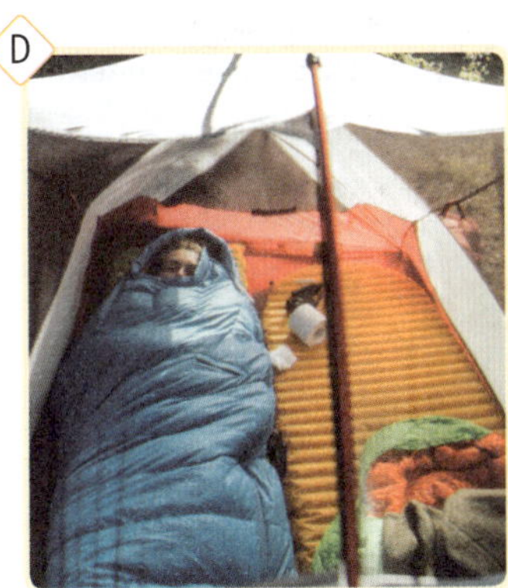

2 Look at the picture on page 92. What do you think happens in the story?

While you read

3 RT4.1 Read and listen to the story. Mark the sentences T (true) or F (false).

1 The story happens on a summer evening. T / F
2 The weather is warm all day. T / F
3 There are holes in the sleeping bags. T / F
4 They leave their dinner and go to the tent. T / F
5 The fox has got their cake. T / F
6 There is only water in the green bag. T / F

4 Read the story again. Complete the sentences with one word in each gap.

1 Katia is on a ______ holiday.
2 She sleeps in a tent with her mother and her ______.
3 Katia wants to get her ______ because she is cold.
4 The ______ eats Katia's food.
5 They haven't got any cake. This is ______ fault.

After you read

5 Look at photos A–D and complete sentences 1–4.

1 We sleep in the ______.
2 We have dinner on a ______.
3 We dry things next to the ______.
4 The ______ makes things wet.

A

plate

B

fire

C

rain

D

evening

6 RT4.2 Listen to the end of Katia's story. Tick (✓) the things that happen.

1 Katia and her family sleep in their car. ☐
2 They go camping in their garden. ☐
3 They find a snake in their tent. ☐

7 What do you think of the story? Colour the stars.

Self-checks answer key

Unit 0 Self-check

Exercise 1
1 12 2 17 3 blue 4 yellow 5 black
Exercise 2
1 ruler 2 notebook 3 chair 4 clock
5 sandwich
Exercise 3
1 They're 2 It's a 3 They're 4 They're
5 It's a
Exercise 4
1 books 2 boxes 3 bins 4 sandwiches
5 trees
Exercise 5
1 please 2 down 3 books 4 pairs
5 up

Unit 1 Self-check

Exercise 1
1 aunt 2 father 3 brother 4 daughter
5 granny/grandmother
Exercise 2
1 park 2 American 3 school 4 France
5 home
Exercise 3
1 are 2 is 3 aren't 4 are 5 am not
Exercise 4
1 my 2 We 3 Ben's 4 your 5 Nadia's
Exercise 5
1 is 2 Hello/Hi 3 Nice 4 meet 5 too

Unit 2 Self-check

Exercise 1
1 boring 2 backpack 3 cap 4 top
5 new
Exercise 2
1 cap 2 mobile phone 3 jeans
4 trainers 5 skateboard
Exercise 3
1 a 2 b 3 b 4 a 5 b
Exercise 4
1 Yes, it is. 2 No, they aren't
3 Yes, we are. 4 No, he isn't.
5 Yes, she is.
Exercise 5
1 d 2 e 3 a 4 f 5 b

Unit 3 Self-check

Exercise 1
1 armchair 2 window 3 cushion 4 sofa
5 garage
Exercise 2
1 bedroom 2 under 3 kitchen 4 next to
5 fridge
Exercise 3
1 are 2 a pen 3 aren't 4 is 5 aren't
Exercise 4
1 isn't 2 Are 3 any 4 aren't 5 a
Exercise 5
1 e 2 f 3 b 4 a 5 c

Unit 4 Self-check

Exercise 1
1 wavy 2 big 3 nose 4 legs
5 helpful
Exercise 2
1 long 2 straight 3 curly 4 friendly
5 clever
Exercise 3
1 Has 2 got 3 Have 4 haven't
5 hasn't
Exercise 4
1 Their 2 his 3 Her 4 Our 5 its
Exercise 5
1 problem 2 mistake 3 all right 4 It's
5 sure

Unit 5 Self-check

Exercise 1
1 jump 2 write 3 swim 4 cook
5 run
Exercise 2
1 play 2 make 3 read 4 ride 5 play
Exercise 3
1 can 2 and 3 but 4 can't 5 can
Exercise 4
1 Yes, she can. 2 Can the dogs sing?
3 No, they can't. 4 Can the boy ride his bike?
5 Yes, he can.
Exercise 5
1 can 2 sure 3 can't 4 problem
5 Great

Unit 6 Self-check

Exercise 1
1 have 2 hang 3 play 4 watch 5 go
Exercise 2
1 August 2 Saturday 3 November
4 April 5 Wednesday
Exercise 3
1 go 2 likes 3 tidies 4 live 5 have
Exercise 4
1 I am usually busy in the afternoon.
2 We never play tennis.
3 Mum sometimes watches TV.
4 He is always late for school.
5 My cat often sleeps on my bed.
Exercise 5
1 past 2 is 3 minutes 4 at 5 clock

Unit 7 Self-check

Exercise 1
1 hamster 2 iguana 3 parrot 4 goldfish
5 rabbit
Exercise 2
1 a fast bird 2 a dangerous lion
3 a slow tortoise 4 an ugly fly
5 a strong elephant
Exercise 3
1 doesn't sing 2 don't live 3 doesn't like
4 don't speak
Exercise 4
1 Does Tom wear jeans to school?
2 No, he doesn't.
3 Do your friends like football?
4 Yes, they do.
5 Does your granny visit you every week?
6 Yes, she does.
Exercise 5
1 you 2 have 3 please 4 that's 5 are

Unit 8 Self-check

Exercise 1
1 taekwondo 2 ice-skating 3 January
4 autumn 5 early
Exercise 2
1 brush 2 play 3 go 4 drink 5 fruit
Exercise 3
1 My sister doesn't like roller skating.
2 Do you like swimming?
3 I love singing.
4 We don't like getting up early.
5 Do your friends like eating pizza?
Exercise 4
1 Where 2 How 3 them 4 her 5 it
Exercise 5
1 like 2 It's 3 it 4 is 5 Me

Pearson Education Limited
KAO Two
KAO Park
Hockham Way
Harlow, Essex
CM17 9SR
England
and Associated Companies throughout the world.

pearsonenglish.com/widerworld2e

First published 2023

ISBN: 978-1-292-42276-3

Set in Frutiger Next Pro
Printed by Talleres Trama S.A., in Argentina

Acknowledgements

The Publishers would like to thank all the teachers and students around the world who contributed to the development of Wider World Second Edition: Milena Aleksić, Tuğba Arslantaş, Gülşah Aslan, Mahgol Baboorian, Katarzyna Beliniak, Burcu Candan, Seri Diri, Hanna Dudich, Sema Karapinar, Nadiia Kasianchuk, Duygu Kayhan, Iryna Kharchenko, Ana Krstić, Ilknur Manav, Fulya Mertoğlu, Ivana Nikolov, Banu Oflas, Duygu Özer, Jagoda Popović, Marija Šanjević, Karmen Irizar Segurola, Elif Sevinç, Ludmila Shengel, Ayşe Sönmez, Anna Standish, Natalia Tkachenko, Pamela Van Bers, Jelena Vračar, Agnieszka Woźnicka, Münevver Yanık.

The Publishers would like to thank the following people who commented on the Wider World Second Edition content: Milena Aleksić, Mahgol Baboorian, Hanna Dudich, Izabela Kołando, Karmen Irizar Segurola, Joanna Srokosz, Anna Zając.

We would also like to thank the authors of the first edition of Wider World whose work has been the basis for creating this adaptation: Kathryn Alevizos, Carolyn Barraclough, Catherine Bright, Sheila Dignen, Lynda Edwards, Rod Fricker, Suzanne Gaynor, Bob Hastings, Jennifer Heath, Liz Kilbey, Stuart McKinlay, Sarah Thorpe, Tasia Vassilatou, Damian Williams, Sandy Zervas.

Photo Acknowledgements

123RF.com: 5second 78, aberration 56, Adilfitree Prapruetsutjarit 34, Adrian Ilie 87, amarosy 25, andreykuzmin 73, Anek Suwannaphoom 76, 78, angel_a 37, Antonio Guillem 20, balefire9 39, belchonock 56, 59, believeinme33 10, Cathy Yeulet 40, claudiodivizia 59, cobalt 32, Danila Krylov 36, Deborah Dixon 93, Dejan Jekic 4, destinacigdem 21, deusexlupus 82, dolgachov 90, domenicogelermo 14, Eric Isselee 76, 81, 81, Erik Lam 40, Everett B Palmer IV 2, ferli 90, fizkes 54, Georgii Dolgykh 4, Golkin Oleg 43, hqrloveq 93, Igor Kovalchuk 77, Igor Plotnikov 59, indigolotos 16, isselee 43, Iuliia Sokolovska 78, jackf 15, jessmine 4, khvost 16, Kwanchai Chai-udom 87, luchschen 59, magone 4, 5, Marco Salomon 56, mavoimage 25, Michael Rosskothen 78, mikelane45 58, milkos 40, monticello 4, NejroN 78, nerthuz 82, nikolaich 50, okan akdeniz 34, Oleksandr Grybanov 56, Olena Mykhaylova 64, Olesia Bilkei 76, Olga Popova 82, paltushyamal 71, Pan Xunbin 75, Pauliene Wessel 34, Photodeti 76, piko72 75, Piotr Adamowicz 50, Richard Thomas 4, Ruslan Gilmanshin 34, saphira 59, scanrail 2, scyther5 2, serezniy 5, 50, Sergei Uriadnikov 91, Sergey Kuznetsov 38, Sergey Lavrentev 56, Sergey Novikov 22, 90, snake3d 5, stefanschurr 58, Suttipon Yakham 81, szefei 5, tarzhanova 25, Tatiana Shevchenko 87, tim2infinity 59, Uladzimir Martyshkin 17, Valentyna Chukhlyebova 78, Valentyna Zhukova 91, Valery Voennyy 50, Vichaya Kiatying-Angsulee 64, vilainecrevette 78, Viparat Kluengsuwanchai 59, Vitaly Korovin 4, Waldemar Dabrowski 81, Wang Aizhong 78, whiskybottle 37, willyambradberry 58, wuttichok panichiwarapun 36, Yongyut Khasawong 25; **Alamy Stock Photo:** Art Collection 2 12, Blend Images 22, dieKleinert 12, Historic Collection 12, Image Source Plus 90, Myrleen Pearson 37, North Wind Picture Archives 12, RTimages 10, Sergey Novikov 90, The National Trust Photolibrary 54, Zoonar GmbH 90; **Datacraft Co Ltd:** Datacraft Co Ltd 38; **Fotolia:** BGodunoff 28, Dmitry Naumov 32, georgerudy 11, 11, MNStudio 14, Tatty 28, venusangel 36; **Getty Images:** 6, 3sbworld/iStock / Getty Images Plus 50, allgord/iStock / Getty Images Plus 17, Bettmann 12, Donald Maclellan/Hulton Archive 12, Hakase_/iStock / Getty Images Plus 55, hanapon1002/iStock / Getty Images Plus 71, heinteh/iStock / Getty Images Plus 17, izusek/E+ 14, jabejon/iStock 25, Jay Blakesbert/ UpperCut Images 47, Lisa Holder / EyeEm 93, Lorado/E+ 71, Milko/ E+ 14, MoMo Productions/DigitalVision 42, Natali-Ka/iStock / Getty Images Plus 71, Peter Mason/Image Source 11, Pornpawit Phosawang / EyeEm 17, Sidekick 24, StratosGiannikos/iStock / Getty Images Plus 71, Synthetic-Exposition/iStock / Getty Images Plus 50, Tempura/E+ 42, triloks/E+ 10, Westend61 10, 93, Анатолий Тушенцов/iStock / Getty Images Plus 93; **Pearson Education Ltd:** Gareth Boden 33, 38, Jon Barlow 2, 6, 7, 19, 20, 21, 29, 37, 39, 51, 83, Jörg Carstensen 66, Jules Selmes 37, Studio 8 20; **Shutterstock:** 86, Aaron Amat 43, Africa Studio 64, Aleksandr Kurganov 21, Aleksey Stemmer 78, Alena Ozerova 40, altanaka 40, Andrienko Anastasiya 39, Anitham Raju Yaragorla 78, Ann Baldwin 5, arapix 17, arka38 25, Atiketta Sangasaeng 36, Atlaspix 15, Baloncici 32, Bildagentur Zoonar GmbH 78, BlackSTAR-FOTOGRAFiE 93, Blend Images 22, BonD80 21, Boris Rabtsevich 10, caimacanul 4, cbpix 76, charnsitr 12, Chintla 32, Chiyacat 25, Christophe Testi 12, 15, Craig Wactor 86, Cultura Motion 34, Deborah Kolb 22, defpicture 39, Denis Radovanovic 20, DenisNata 17, dien 77, Ditty_about_summer 58, Dja65 34, Dmitry Kalinovsky 77, Dudarev Mikhail 50, Dusan Zidar 40, egd 93, Ekaterina V. Borisova 81, ekler 12, Elena Elisseeva 86, Elnur 16, 50, elRoce 59, Eric Isselee 78, 81, Everything 17, Ewelina Wachala 37, 37, Fh Photo 37, Fotofermer 75, Fotogroove 12, 15, Four Oaks 59, Gelpi 54, 62, Globe Turner 12, Golbay 16, goodluz 40, gt29 2, Gunnar Pippel 76, hanzl 82, Hefr 78, Herschel Hoffmeyer 59, Hong Vo 25, Igor Sokolov 82, imagefactory 34, Johan Larson 76, Johannes Kornelius 32, Justina.au 78, kanate 5, Karkas 16, 16, kavring 5, Kesu 76, Kiril Stanchev 14, Kiselev Andrey Valerevich 42, KKulikov 25, Kozlik 47, Lucy Liu 16, Mahathir Mohd Yasin 65, Marco Mayer 32, MariyanaM 75, Mark Herreid 64, mashe 86, Media Guru 32, Melica 56, Michael Kraus 34, Mikadun 37, Mike Flippo 17, 58, Mike Pellinni 5, Mike Workman 43, milatas 10, Mirek Kijewski 81, movit 10, MSPhotographic 17, naluwan 42, Nata-Lia 21, nattanan726 43, Nestor Noci 64, Nik Ryabukhin 93, nikshor 5, nogandosan 64, Nording 82, oksana2010 4, Oleksiy Mark 21, Olga Popova 25, 39, 39, oliveromg 58, Omsickova Tatyana 40, OZaiachin 32, Paul Stringer 12, Phant 5, Photobankgallery 85, polya_olya 14, pun photo 4, Raisa Kanareva 42, rattanapatphoto 39, rzymuR 25, Samuel Borges Photography 64, sanneberg 86, Sashkin 75, SekarB 91, Sergey Peterman 42, Sergii Korshun 38, SFROLOV 69, ShutterStockStudio 64, Sklep Spozywczy 25, smuay 28, Stuart Monk 37, StudioSmart 36, StudioSmile 4, Studiotouch 5, Taiftin 17, Tanya Kalian 71, Tony_C 16, topseller 86, Tracy Starr 91, Tracy Whiteside 22, Tyler Hartl 5, Tyler Olson 50, Utekhina Anna 77, VaLiza 65, virtu studio 50, W. Scott McGill 34, Yeko Photo Studio 34, YK 36

Illustrated by Denis Alonso (Beehive Illustration) 8, 32 (chair), 41 (Exercise 5), 42 (Exercise 1, items 2, 4, 5), 52 (Exercise 5 item 1), 53 (Exercise 4), 80 (Exercise 2 Items 1, 4, 5); Joanna Bernat (Pigeon) 9, 14, 28, 29, 38, 42, 50, 60, 61, 68 ; Ewa Ciałowicz (Pigeon) 51, 55, 58, 72, 82, 84; Michał Domański (Pigeon) 21, 22 (line characters), 32, 33, 34, 36, 88; Gergely Fórizs (Beehive Illustration) 26, 27, 48, 49, 70, 71, 92; Alicja Gapińska 7, 8, 12, 16, 17, 19, 24, 29, 31, 38, 41, 53, 61, 80, 85; Matylda Kozera (Pigeon) 72 ; Beata Krajewska (Studio Gardengraf) 6, 55; Daniel Limon (Beehive Illustration) 44, 66, 83; Adam Linley (Beehive Illustration) 22 (crossword clues), 72 (butterfly); Jim Peacock (Beehive Illustration) 12, 54; Alan Rowe 5, 8, 18, 30, 40, 52, 62, 74, 84; Marcin Rutkowski (Pigeon) 17, 28; Matijos Gebreselassie (Pigeon) 20.